ENERGY MANAGEMENT

How to Increase Your Positive Energy Levels

W9-AZT-786

BARBARA GRAY
STARLIGHT PRODUCTIONS

Dedicated to the high energy
people at Unity North and
Unitymarietta

ENERGY MANAGEMENT™ Seminars

Barbara Gray does training and keynotes on the topic ENERGY MANAGEMENT. You may contact Barbara Gray at 770-971-0179 to receive more information and a course syllabus.

Barbara Gray is the author of *Life's Instruction Books for Women, Volumes I, II, & III, Come Grow With Me, Success Through Spirituality for Women,* and *The Christmas Angels.*

Other Seminar and Keynote Topics

The Spirit-Mind-Body Connection
Utilizing Your Internal Resources: The Power of the Mind
How Stress Creates Illness in the Mind, Body, Spirit
20 Stress Reduction Techniques
The Power of Meditation
You Are Connected Mind, Body, Spirit

Diversity and Sensitivity
Health Care with a Human Touch
The Art of Caring: Empathy and Compassion
 Reclaim the Flame

Energy Medicine
Using Color and Music to Promote Healing
Healing Through Meditation, Visualization, and
Imagery
Leadership for Nurses
Understanding People: Body Language, Faces,
Behavior and Habits
Seeing Change as Leading to Growth and Improvement
Creating a Personal Vision through Imagination and
Affirmations
You Are A Star! (signature speech)

People With Positive High Energy Believe

They believe that one person can make a difference.

They have personal initiative that comes from within and is not dependent on others or circumstances.

They take sole responsibility for their choices, decisions, and actions.

They know that anytime they choose not to be who they really are, they will experience confusion.

They understand the benefits of positive relationships.

They know that their actions attest to what they believe.

They are not constrained by time or space.

They understand the law of cause and effect.

They are visionary.

They believe in abundance.

Foreword

"A new idea is first condemned as ridiculous and then dismissed as trivial, until finally, it becomes what everybody knows."

I feel a passion for the topic Energy Management.

When you feel passion for something, you are willing to give everything for your belief because it rises from your very core. You know that you know. As you teach you are also teaching yourself. You feel a great privilege of sharing what you know. I see the same information shared over and over just written or spoken with different words. Plato talked about these same ideas in the *Phaedrus, Phaedo, and Symposium.* Shakespeare knew about mental energy. The Bible teaches energy principles when it says, "as a man soweth so does he reap." We mean the same thing when we say that you get back what you send out. The Bible tells us to "be a light unto the world," and "to let your light shine." The light the Bible refers to is known to anyone who practices meditation. When the eye is sound, that is, attention is withdrawn inward from the visual field of consciousness, there is often the sensation of the body being full of light, a consciousness of the light-energy out of which the body is composed. When emptied of thoughts, consciousness becomes aware of the light of being itself, the light by which one observes one's own thoughts, awareness, and everything else. Hypocrates said that imagery and physical processes "tread in a ring" constantly influencing one another. We are indeed connected to one another and to everything in the universe.

The principles in this book are the same on which several Nobel Prize winners in physics have based their work. As the author of the book *Energy Management* and the originator of the seminars with the same title, I bring these principles to *light* in the area of self-directed energies.

We can talk about the things that we want in life, but we have to look honestly at where we are putting our energies toward getting those things. This book is to make you aware that *you are energy*, with all the characteristics of light, love, vibration, rhythm, and connection. We receive energy and send out energy in the form of thoughts, words, and emotions. Fear is not inherent in us; it is not our essence. It is a learned emotion that drains our energy. It is the reason why our dreams and plans don't succeed. The belief in fear causes us to use excuses and rationalization and then deny what we know as true. It helps us put off facing the internal lion that stands at the entrance to our peace and happiness and roars. The loud roar of the internal lion keeps us from hearing the still quiet voice and disconnects us from our balancing, attuning, and restorative systems.

This book is going to challenge you to believe that humans can do what machines and technology can do. After all—who invented the machines and technology? Science is telling us that they are close to inventing a chip that is so small that it can be put in our blood system and take pictures. We believe this because we know that chips in technology are getting smaller and smaller. But if I tell you that there are people who are able to scan a person's body with their *third eye,* using it like a camera to see within the body, most likely you will not believe me. But it is true.

People have developed abilities far beyond most of us. Cosmetic companies hire people with such sensitivity to smells that they can distinguish more than 30,000 different smells. We have the same number of taste buds, around 10,000 as wine tasters, but they develop their awareness to such a degree that they are able to tell you the year a wine was produced. Some blind people can tell the color of fabrics by touching them. They can also point to the location of the moon in the sky or touch a turning phonograph record and tell which instruments are playing. Professional athletes speak of experiences where time appeared to stand still, or they were in the flow of the event so much that they knew positively the ball would go in the hole, basket, or someone's hands. Charles Lindbergh wrote in his book *The Spirit of St. Louis* that phantom figures appeared in his airplane during his famous flight across the Atlantic. We've all known friends or family who tell of experiences seeing deceased loved ones.

The point being made here is that each of us can further develop our abilities and our paranormal abilities. The first focus of this book is to show that we are energy beings. The second focus is on the electrical and chemical energy produced by our bodies. The third is teaching people awareness of the electromagnetic field and to be able to see the light, colors, magnetic energy and flux of energies. The last focus of this book is to teach people how to manage their energies.

Energy Management is a generalization and synthesis on the topic that we are energy beings capable of increasing our all of our energy levels. In order to discuss this broad topic fully, the book has to delve into the topics of anatomy, physics, health, spirit-mind-body only as they apply to us as energy beings. All of this is to explain why on one page I speak about how the body's nervous system works as an electrical power source, and on the next page talk about how light shines from our bodies. As the author, I am asking you to make the connection that we are whole beings—spirit-mind-body—capable of doing whole brain thinking and then transforming our mental, physical, and spiritual energy in focused attention to being more productive.

Would you say that you or the company that you work for seeks to know answers intuitively? This thought process is used in very few companies. This explains why some companies make such costly mistakes and why companies feel the need to copy other companies. It is also the reason people make costly mistakes in their lives.

Want to make sure all your projects and decisions are successful? Learn to access your intuition. First, though, you must know that *intuition* is different from an *intuitive feeling*, which can come from emotion and be on a personal level. Intuition comes from higher levels of consciousness and awareness. It is stable and reliable information giving a sense of *knowing that you know*. Most of us have experienced a time when we *knew* the absolute truth from some higher place.

Introduction

ENERGY MANAGEMENT is based on universal principles of how the universe was originally created and how it continues to operate successfully. By simply learning the tools, you will be able to decide how and where you want to expend your energies. Energy Management can be applied to our personal lives and to companies.

Since the 1970s, emphasis has been placed on Time Management—organization based on accomplishing the most *action* in a day. Time Management didn't encourage taking time for creative or intuitive thinking, for self-reflection, and focusing and replenishing our energies so that we might be more productive. *It was all about time...but we are not time beings.*

Let me illustrate my point. Let's pretend you have just had a heart attack in Chicago and you are rushed to the ER. As you are being worked on your heart stops. A new intern says, "Hand me a watch, I need to get his heart started."

Fortunately for you, Dr. Green steps in and says, "He's not a time being, he's electrical!" With that, Dr. Green shocks you with a high voltage defibrillator and starts your heart again.

Stress Management probably came along because of Time Management. We have time regulated ourselves into fatal chronic diseases, heart attacks, cancer, emotional deadness, and plain old tiredness. Dr. Stephen Covey's book, *The Seven Habits of Highly Effective People,* taught people to spend time on those things that are most important, the long-range plans that will have the most effect on us and our businesses.

Technological advances that were supposed to help us save time have made us a slave to time.

We live in the most evolutionary of times— outstanding technological inventions, expansive research on human potential and the power of the mind, and an age of new paradigm shifts in health-care, business, and education.

One problem for companies today is employee information overload. New technology bogs down employees with information processing at the expense of creative thinking. There is a time when we need to empty our minds of all information so that we can create solutions, processes, technologies, and inventions that are beyond what is already being done. Bill Gates' parents said in a recent interview that most of the time when they called to him as a child he replied, "I'm busy thinking." How many real thinkers do you know?

This new millennium will be characterized as an age of transformation, resulting in new freedoms of thoughts and beliefs. Companies who teach their employees Energy Management will teach them how to think intuitively and how to transform negative imploding energy into positive charging energy. When companies encourage employees to do **real thinking** based on intuitive processing and then allow the sharing of that information, they will achieve *being in the zone* or *being in the flow*, the place where creative thought and production take place.

What kind of state is **being in the zone** or **being in the flow?** Some athletes describe it as almost a spiritual experience; others would say that it isn't. Some say it is just a time when everything is going so right that there is no fear of failure. Most employers would like employees who can achieve this state because it means success and productivity. Employers are looking for employees dedicated to their purpose and who are responsible and in control of their mental and emotional states.

Now what does this have to do with our energy level? We're not talking about people who are physically hyperactive or who are operating on nervous energy. We are talking about people who remain calm and in control in all situations. These are people who make good leaders and the kinds of managers and supervisors who raise the vibration of the people they work with. They teach and demonstrate to everyone in their group how working in the flow and being in the zone achieves productivity at its highest level. These are people who are motivated intrinsically and spiritually.

Energy Management teaches us that we are *energy beings,* not just information-gathering computers. By connecting to our energy sources, we can experience powerful and creative lives, and we can be in control of our lives. We are completely capable of and responsible for choosing how we expend our energy.

People seeking to raise their energy level will reconnect with their **matrix**, which is their foundation, their essence, and the source of their dreams and visions. **Reconnection will occur in people who become conscious of the oneness of their spirit-mind-body.** Their intent and attention will be on their expression as beings composed of **light, energy,** and **love.**

These subjective internal resources, light, love, and energy, give us the ability to develop **health and healthy behaviors, positive thoughts and positive actions.** Each of us has a personality, a sense of order, a set of values, and preferences that we use to judge and create our reality. All of these things are influenced by the information that we take in through our five senses. For many this becomes the basis of their belief system while others go further within and seek truth as their basis. We apply our belief system to what we call our Internal Resources.

The purpose of this book is to bring awareness to the gift and power our Internal Resources have to control in our lives. Most of us do not have a clue what our Internal Resources are. They are our **spirit.** They are **thoughts** of our conscious and subconscious mind. They transform thoughts into energy and form. They are our **memories** stored in every cell in our body. They are the unique and specific **talents, gifts and abilities** given to us to fulfill our specific purpose in life.

The fulfillment of your life's purpose is done both at your job and in your time off the job. It does not interfere with your job; it enhances your productivity. If job and purpose are not connected, spending time in self-reflection will lead to the solution.

We access information and energy not only from those around us, but from the universe at large. Unless you are a mushroom and don't need light, you need the energy from the sun and the other stars. Unfortunately, most of the time we let external events and external information based on other people's perception influence our behaviors and thinking.

One of the worst things we do that defeats our success and happiness is to determine our thoughts and actions based on our preconceived biases based on our previous experiences or the experiences of others. For example, many people write a book and assume that they have to have a publisher to print it. They spend a lot of time and energy getting turned down by publish truth is that many authors self-publish and market their own books very successfully while retaining control.

The goal of this book is to help you apply your highest energy level, your highest vibration, to your Internal Resources and your internal world. Our external world is simply a reflection of our internal world. People on a higher plane create a better world. In order to have **balance, synergy,** and **peace** in our lives internally and externally, our thinking, behaviors, and actions must be aligned with our spirit. Then we become creative beings capable of living powerful lives with success in health, happiness, and contentment. It is through the unfolding of our powers that we find meaning in life. Our Creator placed us in a world where we make choices and gave us the Internal Resources to find the right answers.

As we use these resources, we increase our understanding of ourselves and the people around us. It sounds strange, but most of us are not paying attention to our own lives.

"How much time do you spend each day alone and in quiet self-reflection?"

"Where else could you possibly go to get the answers you need to know and know precisely how you feel?"

Some other questions are:
"Are you tired of being tired?"

People who are tired because of depression and hopelessness feel that life is a battle to be fought. They have lost faith in life and in themselves. This is the time to look at the things you are battling over. Are they worth giving your life up for? Are they worth the energy you are giving them? Since you are an energy being, are the things you are battling with worth giving your life for? Wouldn't it be easier to put your energy where it flows easily?

"Do you want to create life or let it happen to you?"
When you act like a victim, you let life happen to you. When you create life, you make the choices that control your life.

"Do you want to know how to control your own thinking?"
How much time each day are you *being still* and doing self-reflection? Are you able to clear your mind of all thoughts so that you can receive intuitive information?

"Do you want to be passionate about life?"
Prior to making your own personal paradigm shifts and following a new set of principles, you must understand your own infrastructure. Do you know the answers to the following questions?

How does our spirit-mind-body operate and integrate as a whole in the areas of connection, alignment, and balance?

Why is it important that we see ourselves as more than mental and physical beings?

How does our perspective change when we say that we are energy beings given Internal Resources to direct and focus our energies?

How does our "hard wiring" permit us to vibrate at higher or lower energy levels?

The Principles of Energy Management

The Principle of Energy

✳ **All energy is one.**

✳ **Everything in the universe is different vibrations of energy.**

✳ **Everything in the universe is unified.**

✳ **Energy takes form in waves that vary depending upon their vibration.**

✳ **All matter is sending energy through space and in all directions.**

✳ **Light, heat, and sound are different modes of vibratory forces.**

✳ **Energy is intelligent.**

✳ **Thoughts, which are energy, are forces created by mind.**

✳ **We are all a part of a cosmos or energy field that is in constant motion.**

✳ **Every mind is a creative center from which rhythms of energy are going out in all directions.**

✳ **The same principles apply to humans and all matter.**

✳ **Scientists now believe even matter that appears dead or solid emits energy.**

The preceding facts about energy are the basis of our universe and everything in it. Gravity, electromagnetism, and strong and weak atomic forces are all from one basic energy. Atomic energy, solar energy, and love are different aspects of the same unified energy. Everything in the universe is composed of atoms. We are composed of atoms so the same principles that apply to the universe apply to us. We know that the principles of the universe work. If there weren't a gravitational force we would be randomly floating out into space. Energy stays in flux; it moves in particles and waves. It changes form, but it is never destroyed.

To understand anything in this book, you have to conceptualize yourself as an energy being, in that energy flows in and throughout **your** electromagnetic field. You have the ability to allow that energy to flow into your body at a high rate of vibration, or you can block the flow. We have the *choice* of the amount of energy we want.

You have seen on TV thousands of Chinese practicing *chi gung and tai chi.* Even in the U.S. the practice is growing. *Chi* is translated as our vital energy or force and goes back to 3,000 B.C. *Prana* is the Sanskrit word for "vital energy," and awareness of it goes back to 5,000 B.C. The Greek Pythagoras called it *pneuma* and described it as a luminous body that could produce cures. In the 1940's George De La Warr developed radionics instruments to detect radiation in living tissue. From 1970-1989 Robert Becker measured the direct current control system on the human body.

What we call energy medicine is the transmission of electrical, magnetic, or other forms of physical energy called *prana, chi, orgone* or *life force.* Yet every time a news program does a report on alternative healings, such as hands on healing, prayer, or imagery they also interview a medical doctor who tries to refute the findings by always saying that there haven't been enough studies, or there isn't enough proof. Energy in the body has been known about for over 5,000 years.

The proof is standing there alive due to some alternative medicine despite the fact that the medical community had given up on them. A doctor of oncology was himself dying of cancer until he tried a form of alternative medicine. He became a believer. He said he didn't know how it worked, but it did. Anyone can find out whatever they want.

The first law of creation is that everything proceeds from the same one source, the same energy–Spirit. Where are all the negative energies, you might ask? Negative energies are all lumped under one feeling and that is *fear*, or the absence of love. Fear is something that *we* have created.

This Principle of Energy contains a second law, the **Law of Vibration** that states that everything in the universe moves, vibrates and travels in circular patterns. The same principles of vibration in the physical world apply to our thoughts, feelings, desires, and wills. Hopefully, you will learn to increase your awareness when you learn that each **sound, object, and even thought has its own unique vibrational frequency.**

The Law of Vibration

* Everything in the universe is composed of energy and is in motion.
* Light, heat, magnetism, electricity and sounds are forms of vibratory motion.
* Each thing that exists has its own unique vibrational frequency.
* Everything in our universe moves in an elliptical fashion. The myriad of star systems move in elliptical, spiral formation.   The planets in our solar system orbit the sun in elliptical orbits.
* Energy travels in a elliptical fashion; therefore, what goes around comes around.

❋ Energy can neither be created nor destroyed. Energy
    can only be transformed from one form of energy
    into another.
❋ The magnetic lines, such as the electrical fields
    around our earth, flow in circular movement.

Physicists teach us that quantum fields are the
deepest known levels of our natural world. A quark is
defined as the smallest unit of light, electricity, or other
energy that exists. *Quantum* in Latin means "how
much?" The smallest bits of subatomic matter are
vibrations of energy that have taken on the appearance
of solidity but are not solids.

Quantum physics shows that stars, galaxies,
mountains, and trees are connected by infinite, eternal,
unbounded quantum fields. The hard edges of any
object only appear as illusions. These unlimited quantum fields gave us X-rays, transistors, superconductors,
and lasers. The unified field is a single super-field that
is the ultimate reality that underlies all of nature. We
are a part of this whole multiplicity of nature that comes
together in one field.

The Real "Who We Are"

Whether we are creating individually or creating
as a company or group, hopefully, we want to create
solutions for the world to be a better place. We need to
ask ourselves, "What is the energy that drives this
person, business or organization **to** or **from** creating?"

Some people are still focused on only getting
their individual needs met. However, the forward
thinkers will choose to see the world as large worldwide
communities. They will focus on our similarities rather
than our differences. These people will ***honor*** their

relationships. It will be done on an energetic basis, a giving and receiving of positive energies.

An electromagnetic, energetic field encapsulates the physical body. Invisible energy enters our electromagnetic field and, depending on the way that we are open to it, we either allow or disallow that energy to come through. Energy comes in the form of light, vibration, in waves and particles. This is the basis and substance of this book.

We are told to always be *who we are*, but in my speaking career and interaction with people, I don't meet people who have a clue that the *"who we are"* is *energy beings*. Light and love are two other forms of the energy that we are.

Look at the phrases we use to describe people. We note that people have a high or low energetic level. We say that some people take all the energy out of us, while being around others energizes us. Some are called magnetic, others draining. We speak of some people being on a higher plane, meaning that they vibrate at a higher spiritual level. We feel bad "vibes" from people who are thinking negatively or are about to harm us. Our gut feelings send us information in past-present-future form about everything going on in our lives. Another word for gut feelings is intuition—that small still voice inside of us that is intelligent, the one we benefit from when we listen to it.

We describe people in terms of light and different colors of light when we say they are shining and luminous, or we say that they have a dark cloud over their head. By feeling and acting loving, we create a pink cloud over our heads. Two people in love will produce a rosy glow of light, and we feel good just being around them. A jealous person will send out a slimy, dark green light. Ever been in a state of depression and notice that you are choosing to wear dark colors every day?

You may have heard that we don't actually *see* colors. The brain relates to the vibrational frequency of colors. Each color vibrates at a different rate. Red, for example, vibrates at a lower frequency than orange and orange vibrates at a lower rate than yellow. When we can talk about white light—a combination of all of the colors—we are talking about the highest rate of vibration and energy to the visible eye. So do you talk about the light above a person's head as light or energy? The challenge reoccurs when you talk about a person's electromagnetic field. Our thoughts and emotions are forms of energy that are visible in the faint, diffused colored light **in** us and **around** us.

Actually, the first thing is to get people to believe that there is colored light around them. I teach people in a few seconds how to see the colored lights produced in their electromagnetic field. First, you get a person to stand about 18 inches in front of an off-white wall. The use of lamplight is best in the room. The observer stands about ten feet away, unfocuses their eyes, and then casually looks around the person's head and body. Different colors of light, or maybe just one color of light, appear depicting their physical, emotional and mental states at the present moment. It's easy! The few skeptics, the ones who have already decided they can't see light around someone, find that they indeed can't because they decided they couldn't. You see what you expect, and you expect what you invite. What we perceive is strictly our own. We *invite* information to come inside of us or we shut it out.

So far in this book I have been referring to the human energy field or the electromagnetic field instead of using the word aura. It is the most phenomenal thing to me that something people have been seeing since the first man appeared on earth is considered weird. And only this morning on TV, I heard John McEnrow, of all people, talk about another tennis player's aura. Auras are so commonplace that comedians are using them in their jokes.

Eventually you will go to the doctor and he will check out your aura like he checks out your heartbeat. Darkness or redness appears in the aura when and where you have an illness. The word "heal" has the same root as "whole" and even "holy." To be "wholed" is to "re-member," or to bring together all the scattered members which comprise the many parts and levels of our being. The energy field, the aura, surrounds the bodies of all living things. In the springtime you can look about the trees as the new leaves are growing and see the energy field.

We've all gone into a house or room, shivered and felt the coldness because there was so much negative energy. Just as a house becomes saturated with your smell, it becomes saturated with your energy. The pictures on my off-white den walls have green light emitting from them. The pictures at the church I attend have pink light, representing love and purple light, representing God glowing from them. My minister is aglow in purple light.

Teachers should learn to see their students' auras and then they would know if a student were in a state of depression or about to commit suicide, a leading cause of teen-age deaths. The two boys who committed the murders at Columbine High probably had black in the second level of their auras, representing depression, and dark red colors, indicating anger. If you aren't convinced by now that we have light around us, go check out pictures of Jesus and Mary in your Bible and in Renaissance paintings (The Age of Enlightenment). Auras are also referred to as halos. One final word—if you are alive, you have an aura.

To the doubters I say, "Have you ever seen an atom, a proton, or an electron? Yet you believe they are real, even though they are so small you can't see them." There are hundreds of books discussing the electromagnetic field, but most of us haven't been taught about it. UCLA is researching the electromagnetic field.

In addition to colored light being around your head and body, there is a funnel of white light spiraling above your head. It is real and able to be seen by other people. You can see it in your aura. If you live alone, you can look in a mirror. This is the energy we receive from the universe. Light/energy from the stars and the sun enters our bodies at the crown of our head, also through our skin and through our eyes. The sun is just the star that happens to be closest to us.

We raise our energy level, mentally and physically, by allowing more light into our bodies. The more open we are the more light enters. The state of openness occurs in several different ways in our body. We have metabolic energy systems that receive energy that we will discuss later. Right now we want to focus on opening our minds to be "enlightened" and receive information. When we are *open,* we transform ourselves into a person with the ability of "whole-seeing," having the ability to visualize the invisible, to see *what is,* rather than what is expected or conditioned. The result is that we understand our ability to create what we want. When we relinquish fear, we permit our energies to flow.

The high-energy person is able to focus his attention and intention in a relaxed way, to become focused in the object of his contemplation. He becomes a visionary and can deal with many complex ideas at the same time. Remember, there is a distinction between energy at a high level that is used productively and just *using* a lot of misdirected energy.

What is it that is keeping us from vibrating at a higher level, having mountaintop experiences? Our first answer is, "We have problems." Who doesn't? The problem is that we are looking to someone else to rescue us from our problems, while we **know that the solution is found within us.** How much time and energy do we spend thinking *about* ourselves, rather than *from* ourselves? We can get away from the people who we *feel* are our tyrants by moving to a new location, but we can never escape our inner tyrants because we take them with us. Step off the airplane in a new city and the inner tyrants are staring us in the face. The song goes, "You can run, but you can't hide."

The people who do not control their thinking and their emotions are the ones with the bursts of anger and who have battles with depression or anxiety. We hear them say, "I'm not really myself." And they are not. Look at the person with whom you have the greatest conflict. If you look very deeply, you will find that they are people who feel slighted and powerless. Because they feel powerless, they feel the need to control other people. They are people out of control in their own lives. You will never win an argument with this kind of person. When you give them what they desire, which is significance, then you will know how to get along with them. "The solution is to rise above the problems. Why feel bad, why suffer when you don't have to? Stop looking for the easy way out." The problem is that we have been told for so long that we are weak and powerless that we actually believe it. This book is inviting you to read about how your spirit-mind-body is already programmed to work optimally in order for you to increase your mental and physical energy. It suggests ways to make the necessary changes to allow your energy to flow.

We Are Vibrational Beings

We are connected to the unified field by invisible threads composed of faint vibrations.

* We are whirling masses of energy and consciousness.
* Our bodies replicate the movement of the solar system. If you looked into a microscope at a single cell you would see organelles flowing around the nucleus of the atoms in a circular motion.
* Even the various organs in your body have a their own unique vibration.
* All of these cells working together create us as energy beings of Light.

Science and medicine are learning more each day about The Universal Law of Vibration. We achieve awareness through the manifestations of light, heat and sound—all different modes of vibratory forces. All objects even those that appear to be solid, such as rocks and metals, have an inter-molecular rhythm that sends out wave movements in all different directions. Our own human bodies are sending out ceaseless and endless vibrations and they are receiving endless and ceaseless vibrations from the universe. When we understand that everything in the universe is an energy sending and receiving station for all of the energies of the universe, then we understand and hold the belief in the one primal energy—or what we call Infinite Mind, Supreme Intelligence, God, and Love. Yes, *Love is an electromagnetic force.*

Each of us must understand the pervasiveness and power of universal energy. To see ourselves as pure energy enables us to understand being created in the "image" of Universal Mind. If everything in the universe is energy and we are composed of pure energy, then we are an integral part of everything in the Universe. Understanding this enables us to have a sense of being a higher, spiritual self. It is through our Internal Resources, our minds, emotions, spirits, all wrapped up as our gifts, talents, and abilities, that we are the embodiment of our thoughts and the manifestation of our expressions.

The following is one of best demonstrations I use when I speak about our power to influence people with our energy. I chose Larry as a participant out of the audience because he was a perfect physical specimen. A former police officer, he was about six foot four and extremely muscular. After he was introduced to the audience, I asked him to go out of the auditorium so he couldn't hear. Then I told the audience to send him positive thoughts when I put my hands through my hair and to send him negative thoughts when I touched my nose. Larry was asked to return to the stage. I asked him to extend his strong arm out to his side as I secretly signaled the nine hundred people in the audience to send him positive thoughts. I tried unsuccessfully to pull his arm down. Then I secretly signaled the audience to send him negative thoughts. Larry and the audience were shocked that I was now able to easily pull his arm down! This is a great demonstration of how we can influence other people's energy and power with our mental energy. What if everyone at your company united their mental, physical and spiritual energies toward common goals?

Everyone has seen a sonogram of a baby in the mother's womb. The machine works on the principle of sound vibration. The machine *appears* to be seeing inside the mother but what it is actually doing is sending sound vibration at a certain level that picks up the baby's vibration and this is what is being reflected on the screen. Did you know that there are people who are so sensitive to vibration that they are also able to *see* inside a person and detect the vibration of a tumor, to sense illness or actually see illness in the body? Why do we believe that X-ray machines and sonograms can *see* inside of bodies and we don't believe that people can also do it? A human who understood the principle of vibration created the machines.

The **Law of Rhythm** states that everything vibrates and moves in certain rhythms. These rhythms establish seasons, cycles, stages of development and patterns. If you ever tried to go against these rhythms, you learned a real lesson in wasted energy.

Ever complain that the same old things keep happening to you? Are you sending out the same old things? The thoughts, feelings, words, and actions that we send out, we get back. Every premise, thought and example in this book is based on what has just been stated about energy. All humans have four kinds of energy to use in creating the future in which they wish to live—**thoughts, feelings, words, and actions.** You must personally manage these four types of energy so that you are a quantum energy being.

You know we have no private thoughts! They are visible through our bodies and our actions. Thoughts are energy and our thoughts produce our visions that then turn into form. Our mind is in continuous thought. Even when we are sleeping, we are creating our own reality.

You are a Crystalline Energy Being

Crystals are forms of energy created and purified deep in the earth by compression and heat. They are used as transformers of energy in mechanical devices such as clocks, radios, and machinery.

You are a crystal—an energy transformer. Your energy may be either low or high, but you have always been putting out energy. Like crystal formations you are multisided **and** you take in the energies of the things around you—positive or negative. Crystals must be cleansed of the impurities they have taken on. We must also remove impurities and toxins from our spirit-mind-body in order to operate at quantum energy.

Can you see yourself as a crystal prism as you read this book? Picture a ray of white light hitting a prism then diffusing into all of the colors of the rainbow. Remember that colors are just a form of energy, subtle diffusions of white light, vibrating at different levels. Rainbow colors begin at the lowest vibratory level, red, and then move upward to the highest vibratory level, purple. When the body gives off different colors of light, including white light, we call it metabolism. In plants we call it photosynthesis. **We are living photocells**. The body gives off light in reflection of the way we utilize energy. We either allow it to traverse our being, without controlling it, or we attempt to control it and stifle our being. This then becomes evident in the way that the body re-emanates, or re-radiates, this light. The colored light around our bodies can be seen with Kirlian Photography, a technique explained further at the end of this book. Most of us can just unfocus our eyes and see the colors, however.

It is important that you are able to understand and discern your own field of energy. This is when you will be able to control your own life. The person who is aware of his own energies—thinking (mental energy), feelings (emotional energy), and able to connect to their spiritual energy is then able to raise his energy level. The aware person monitors every word and can thereby communicate more accurately and understand the words and actions of others more clearly.

We Are Energy Beings

To understand the Principles of Energy Management, we must reframe our paradigm of who we are and how we operate. Intellectually, we know that we are more than a solid block of matter/body—but most us believe and then act from the belief that we are just physical beings.

Our perspective totally changes when we believe from our core being that *we are energy*. People compliment us by saying, "I like your energy!" We are energy beings operating every aspect of our lives through electrical and chemical energy. Our thoughts produce electrical and chemical energy and create everything we say, do, and experience. We are what we think. The result of our thoughts put into action as electrical and chemical energy becomes our physical manifestation.

Do you realize the significance of realizing that you are **self-directed energy?** How many thoughts do you think you have in a minute? Since there are sixty seconds in a minute, and you could conceivably have more than one thought per second—well it's mind-boggling. I've read that we have 60,000 thoughts per day. More important than the number is the fact that **each thought** becomes something; it does not just float aimlessly out in space. Thoughts are formed within your electromagnetic field and mesh with the universe's electromagnetic field. The big deal is that you have the power to direct your thoughts at those things and people that you are connected to. Picture in your mind some superhero with laser beams of light shining out of his eyes. We even make the statement, "If looks could kill." What if you had to go to court and defend your thoughts just like you have to defend your actions? When you focus your attention on someone, you focus your eyes on him and you are directing your thoughts to them. You are using your energy to influence them. The person who utilizes their internal strength won't be affected but the person who thinks their strength comes externally will. A baseball player up to bat at an out of town game has a choice of whether he will be influenced by the 20,000 fans of the opposing team, all directing their eyes and energy at him and hoping that he will strike out. Why do you think some teams play so much better at home?

You have that same ability. You can be supportive or unsupportive. The receiver decides whether to take in your energy just as you can decide whether you want to receive other people's energy. The problem is that most of us don't know how to receive or stop the energy flow. Think about the most negative person in your office and how you **think** they can ruin your day.

They tell us that we can't change other people— not true! We change people all the time when what we say to them resonates with their belief system or their core being. We send out energy in the form of a thought and they are *open* to it because they are already holding the same thought or belief within themselves. This act creates a connection between us; we are "tied into each other." For example, you are having an argument with someone who is acting anything but loving. However, they are still connected down deep with their core being, which says that they are loving and you choose to send them love. They can not help but connect with you. You already know that we send out our energy through touch, words, thoughts, and behaviors. The point is that we have an awesome responsibility to first know our own essence and then to express it. You are awesome power.

Our Electromagnetic Field

An electromagnetic field exists in and around us. Actually, we could be more accurately described as an electromagnetic field containing spirit-mind-body. It holds the template of our body. Our mind is also in this field. Do you see that the thoughts of our mind create at the same time the body's template and this leads to the physical manifestation of our spirit-mind-body? We think of ourselves as being from skin to skin. Actually we exist in an electromagnetic sphere that may be up to six feet wide. This is the reason many of us feel so uncomfortable crowded into an elevator. We feel uncomfortable when some people get into our space.

Simultaneously, the electromagnetic field knows and feels what's occurring in our internal and external world. We call this state that magic word *consciousness or awareness.* We take information into our electromagnetic field via our senses and intuition concurrently while we are transmitting energy out into the atmosphere as a field of information. It is a choice to stay in a state of unconsciousness.

The electromagnetic field is a visible expression and proof that what we are thinking and feeling can be under our control. Each thought takes form through the light we send out. At the same time the thought is manifesting throughout our bodies through the cells of our body, the circuit system of the mind energy.

Devices such as the electrocardiograph (EKG), and the superconducting quantum inference device (or SQUID, a very highly sensitive magnetometer) are used to scientifically prove and measure the electromagnetic field. The SQUID is used to detect (the magnetoencephalogram, or MEG.) Dr. Robert Becker, an orthopedic surgeon in New York, discusses in his book, *The Body Electric,* that we have measurable patterns of direct currents of electricity that flow over and through the body. The premise of *Energy Management* is based on his research and the research of other scientists that states that the pattern shapes and strengths of the body's complex electrical field change with physiological and psychological changes. All this is to say that what has been known for centuries, that **we have a measurable electromagnetic field,** is now a proven fact.

Our spirits are connected in our own spirit-mind-body by the energy and chemicals that travel through our nervous system, connective tissue system, and blood system. Scientists have called the energy and chemicals, life force fluids, by the names, *prana, chi, orgone, ectoplasm, and bioplasma.* There are many names because the words come from many different cultures. They all are referring to the energy of life, the slow frequency latent essence, which is available in all life forms and in all states of awareness.

What is happening to us is going on in our energy field. You feel another person's evil intentions long before they do something bad to your physical body. Ever gotten "the cold shoulder?" We've been around people who "made our skin crawl," or "who sent chills up our spine." It appears as if only the skin takes in sensory input, such as heat, cold, pain, and pleasure.

Actually, our electromagnetic field receives all of this information and sends out warmth, energy, and light…or it can send out cold, negative energy.

You will read later in the book about how we are information transformers and transmitters. As transformers we draw or magnetize the information that we desire to receive. Our reception of that information is individual. For instance, four people can listen to the same musical note, but one person is deaf, one person is far away from the note, and one person is tone deaf. The fourth person is a piano tuner and he will hear the note accurately. Each person will have a different perception about the same note that he heard.

Our Magnetic Connection

An electromagnetic field contains both an electrical field and a magnetic field. All electromagnetic fields are *force fields*, carrying energy and capable of producing an action at a distance. Rather than the victims we choose to portray we are really *force fields.* Ever thought of yourself as a *force field?*

Parents are always connected to their children whether the children are near or far away. The connection between a mother and child or twins is always especially strong. Mothers often report knowing when something wrong is happening to their children no matter where they are. The connection between twins, whether they've grown up together or apart, is remarkable. When one twin dies, the other twin feels the loss the rest of their life. The point is that mothers and twins report being able to influence far away. We are all connected to other people. Who hasn't received a phone call from a person because he had been thinking about him, or doing what we call directing energy?

The magnetic and electromagnetic fields surrounding our bodies have energy, can carry information, and are produced by electrical energy. Our bodies are animated by alternating periods of contraction and release with accompanying buildups and discharges of electric current. We emit a magnetic field from our spirit-mind-body that reflects what is happening inside us. Ever complain that bad things keep happening to you? Perhaps you are attracting those things by the thoughts you are having.

The electrical currents the spirit-mind-body produces emanate from the brain as well as in every cell of the body. Spirit-mind-body also produces a magnetic field that extends outside the body. We say that we "draw people or objects to us," "birds of a feather flock together," and we "magnetize our dreams and goals."

These electromagnetic fields have characteristics of both waves and particles that are called photons. Photons carry energy. Energy has a wave motion and is sent out at the same speed as light—186,000 miles per second.

Let's look at the energy the eye receives in the form of light. Remember light is just a form of energy. When light enters the human eye, one photon gives up its energy to the retina which then converts it into the electrical signal that produces the **sensation of light.** We don't actually see colors; we sense colors by their energy vibrations. Those with higher frequencies have more energy than those having lower frequencies.

The frequencies of electromagnetic waves or fields are shown on an electromagnetic spectrum. About three-fourths of the way up the spectrum is light. **All light is the same thing as a magnetic field.** It is produced by the movement of electrons and has the same characteristics as the earth's magnetic field, radio waves, and X-rays. All living things sense and derive information from the natural magnetic field of the Earth.

Flowing electrical current produces a magnetic field and light in the space around it. So we are not just magnetic but we are also light beings. An atom is the smallest unit of matter and has all the characteristics of that element. It consists of a dense positively charged nucleus surrounded by a system of electrons. Molecules are composed of atoms. A molecule is composed of several atoms, each surrounded by its own electromagnetic field. When the atoms of an object such as a magnet are lined up in the same direction, the individual magnet fields combine to produce a big field.

Hopefully you will think of the hard wiring of your body—your nervous system, your circulatory system, and your blood system—when you read this next information. **When an electrical current flows in a wire, the movement of the electrons produces a similar field in space and one that is oriented around the wire.** If the electrical current in the wire is fluctuating, the magnetic field will have the same fluctuations.

As energy beings we always have energy flowing through us. If we don't, that means that our physical body is dead. As a professional speaker I have talked to hundreds of nurses who they tell me stories of seeing bright light leaving a person's body at the moment of death. We are energy beings and energy continues its movement and is never destroyed.

The magnetic field is thus characterized on the basis of the rate or frequency of fluctuation. As energy beings our rate of energy fluctuates. If the current is a DC current, the magnetic field is steady like that from a permanent magnet. The strength of the magnetic field depends upon the amount of current flowing in the wire—the more current there is the stronger the magnetic field will be. Doctors say that the information that we take in through our senses goes in a one-way direction that then travels through our nervous system that we might compare to DC current. If all the systems of our bodies, meaning the circulatory system, blood system, nervous system, endocrine system, and muscular system, are functioning properly and are open, then we receive all the energy possible. The individual cells of these systems are either functioning properly or improperly and determine our level of energy and health.

Let's use the air that we breathe to illustrate this. Oxygen, a form of energy, travels through our blood system. When the cells that form the muscles are constricted, say by lack of physical activity, blood does not flow well through them and they hold stagnated toxins. In the same way that fire cannot burn without oxygen, our bodies do not produce as much **energy or light** without enough oxygen. We are like the burning candle that produces energy in the form of light and heat. All this information is in preparation to seeing yourself as an energy being we already know of as exuding heat, but also exuding light.

The total body effects of external fields are mediated through two highly specific and sophisticated internal organs: the magnetic organ which is closely connected to the central nervous system, and the pineal gland, which is part of the brain. Our "magnetic organ" is located high up at the back of the nasal passage just in front of the pituitary gland. Many humans have an innate ability to sense the direction of magnetic north. A friend named Bonnie told me that her father always asked her directions as a child regardless of whether she had been to the location or not. She simply *felt how to get there.* Humans and other animals have magnetite crystals that aid them in sensing the direction of the Earth's magnetite. After you read about our electro-magnetic field later in the book, you will understand the importance of knowing that **the *body* is inside the *mind*, not the other way around.** We have a mind field of energy, a nonlocalized area of intelligence that creates what appears as a physical entity.

Studies have shown that the mind is distributed and acts in every part of our bodies. The mind is in the cells of our brain, our blood, our fluids, our internal organs, our muscles, our bones, and our skin—in each of the 100 trillion cells of our bodies. Thought is produced all over our bodies. So when we have the *thought* of fear, our bodies react from head to toe. The hypothalamus secretes chemicals into the blood which circulates into the pituitary gland, which releases a second chemical (ACTH). This, of course, activates the adrenal glands. Some of the blood in our body leaves our skin and goes elsewhere in preparation for flight. Our breathing deepens and accelerates, the heart rate increases, and the blood pressure rises. It is not neces-sary to go into every activity that takes place when fear enters our minds; we've all been there. But it shows that the sensations that enter our bodies through our skin and the other four senses affect our thoughts and every cell throughout our bodies at the precise same moment.

Your mind is in constant action every microsec-ond creating mind energy. The body responds by creating the appropriate chemical information sub-stances. You can wake up from a deep sleep and know that your sub-conscious mind is working. We call this mental chatter, and it goes on in the conscious and sub-conscious levels. Since your mind is working all night, why not ask your mind for answers to questions before you go to sleep? You can be awakened in the morning with the perfect solution to your questions. We know that each person experiences about sixty thousand thoughts per day. Unfortunately, 95% of today's thoughts are the same as they were yesterday and tomorrow's will also be the same. This book will teach you how to control your mental chatter and how to produce productive mental energy.

The mind exists **throughout** the body and the level at which the spirit-mind-body works is directly related to your state of consciousness (awareness). We communicate with the fields of order, the operating laws of everything in the universe: balance, alignment, connection, and vibration and energy. The spinal cord is the central conductor of electrical impulses.

We are aligned, unified, and included as one with all things at the level we choose to experience our consciousness. This is the pathway through which we create and express. We have always known that we have emotions that create our moods and influence our energy levels, but who has seen an emotion? We certainly see their results.

The Principle of Spirit-Mind-Body Oneness

"The spirit is the life, the mind the builder, and the physical is the result." Edgar Cayce

In the process of seeing old unconscious patterns, we may re-awaken memories, emotions, or experiences that were too painful for us to look at the time. In terms of our awareness there is an outer vision, how we see the world, and an inner vision, how we see ourselves. The clearer we can see inside ourselves, without denial, the clearer our outer vision will become. Light seems to be able to cut through the roadblocks and resistances we have set up, such as, ego, personality, and the rational mind and helps us discover unconscious patterns about ourselves. It is as though light fills up all the dark places of the inner vision. When we look at light, what we see is a clear mirror of ourselves.

Dr. Samuel Berne

The Split

Our faulty thinking has not only led us to think of ourselves as separate and divided from the rest of reality; it has also misled us into thinking of ourselves as divided into separate, exclusive parts of spirit-mind-body. Our habits of divisive, dualistic thinking are so strong that we conceive of ourselves not as a unity, but as a temporary union of disparate, opposed elements. We think of ourselves as **having** a body and a soul, or as **having** a body and a mind, although **who** it is who

has these things is not something we are prepared to think about.

This dualistic thinking, seeing things in terms of opposites, has its roots far back in the development of western culture. Light and dark, good and evil, matter and spirit, body and soul, these are just a few of the oppositions imbedded in our language and thought. The ancient Greeks conceived of the soul as a separate entity that inhabited the body for a time and left it at the time of death, a concept that was passed down to Christianity. Rene Descartes, the seventeenth century French philosopher, asserted that human beings are composed of two distinct components, the body and the mind, that are associated together, and this Cartesian mind-body split has had a profound influence on Western thought.

But today we are beginning to understand that the things we call mind, body, and spirit are merely different aspects of one and the same thing and that there are no clear boundaries between them. The human being, like the universe, is a unity, not just a loose union or temporary affiliation of distinctly different parts.

The human being is a whole, integrated being composed of three things: light, energy, and love. The great prophet and psychic, Edgar Cayce, made the following affirmation to God, "We are as lights in thee." He said of the spirit-mind-body connection, "The Spirit is the life, the mind is the builder, the physical is the result. We are first essence, which gives rise to consciousness that gives rise to mind that gives rise to matter." To understand that matter or the physical is a product of our own creations is most powerful. More powerful is to understand, "We are all that there is, all that there is, is within us. By exploring our inner landscape, we also explore the universe."

The mind-body split has profound and destructive consequences. When the mutual influence of the mind and body on each other is neglected, disharmony results and the mind and body can even go to war with each other. When the body is conceived of as simply a vehicle for the "real self," it can be neglected or abused. On the other hand, when a person identifies himself too much with the body, he does not develop his higher faculties and remains too much the slave of instinct and appetite or remains trapped at a level of physical vanity and material greed.

But the real question for us is not to arrive at a philosophical understanding. The real question is, how do we, in practical terms, heal the mind-body split? How do we bring spirit-mind-body into harmony so that our new understanding of their unity has practical results for us? How do we use the power of the mind and spirit to help heal and keep healthy the body, and how do we use the body to promote our inner growth as beings of mind and spirit? These are the real issues, and we want practical methods, not just fine-sounding theories.

The Body

The ways our bodies are unique

1. Fingerprints: There is less than one chance in 64 billion that two fingerprints are the same. It is impossible for a whole set of fingerprints to be alike.
2. No two faces are exactly alike.
3. A printed replica of an electronically recorded voiceprint proves each speaker is distinct.
4. Our handwriting is unique. Handwriting can be forged, but the person must be an expert.

5. Bloodhounds can pick up the scent of one person out of a million.
6. Brain-wave patterns are entirely distinctive.
7. Human infants are born with unique and identifiable rhythms of sleeping and waking. A newborn's breathing pattern is as distinctive as a thumbprint.
8. Every cell in the body contains molecules of DNA on which is written the blueprint for the entire body.
9. Even the irises of our eyes are different.

The following is the answer to the question posed in the introduction:

How can we open the body's internal pathways and keep the energy flowing?

How the Nervous System Works

The human nervous system is composed of the brain, the spinal cord, and a network of nerves that branch out through the body. The nerves extend from head to toe and information about every habit you have follows the route from the brain to the area of the body concerned. All bodily activities are thus controlled. This communication goes on day and night, whether you are awake or asleep. The maze of nerves that forms the network of sensory input decides which information to pass on to the brain, unless there is interference by the intellect.

Anyone can train himself to break the pattern and reverse the process of automatic nervous reaction. When conscious intelligence tells the nervous system what to accept and what to reject, we can become masters of our habits. The cerebral cortex is largely responsible for decision making. The cortex is taught to

desensitize the nerves dependent upon harmful substances. Actions and habit responses will reflect negative conditioning until the nervous relay syndrome is
deliberately changed on a subconscious level. Every
automatic habit and personal idiosyncrasy originates in
the brain.

The brain is a presence in the immune system.
Tendrils of the nerve tissue run through almost all the
important sectors of the immune system: thymus gland,
bone marrow, lymph nodes, and spleen. The hormones
and neurotransmitters the brain secretes and controls
have an affinity for immune cells. Certain states of
mind and feelings can have powerful biochemical
aftershocks.

The body's autonomic nervous system has a
web-like network designed to broadly send out electrical stimulations. We know the misery of feeling disconnected. All of the autonomic cell bodies and ganglia
are located in the body cavity outside the spinal cord
and the anatomical boundaries of the central nervous
system. These interconnections appear to be a loose,
wandering meshwork, but like everything else in the
body, there is organization.

The autonomic nervous system is not self-
governing at all. Its functions are integrated with
voluntary movements, and with motivations and effects.
One's experiences from moment to moment dictate not
only the contractions of one's skeletal muscles, but also
large functional shifts in the body's internal organs. Our
bodies are the world's highest sense-perceptors, if we
will listen to them. We call this awareness.

It has been written that the body is just a dumb
animal that follows the direction of the mind. Not true.
The spirit-mind is in every cell of our body. Our bodies
have spirit-mind wisdom. The spirit-mind-body is an

intelligent system that involves a massive and rapid simultaneous exchange of energy that contains information.

The body is a psychosomatic network. Let me clarify the exact meaning of the word "psychosomatic." Somatic simply refers to the body. All of the words which originate with psyche (mind)—psychiatrist, psychic, psychological—are based on the connection of the mind to the soul (spirit). Understanding the oneness of spirit-mind-body will **increase your energy flow**.

The body is also an interdependent web of relationships, none of which is more important. You must know how the body's information-network systems—circulatory, musculature, immune, endocrine, and nervous—work in order to stay in a state of homeostasis (health, balance and harmony). Each of these systems is an energy system. They receive energy from food, water, breathing, and light. The information systems tell you when they need more or less of these elements. If you will listen, you will be able to **increase your energy flow**.

We think that we can keep secrets about our past and our present, who we are, what we are thinking in the present moment a secret. It is erroneous to think that because we are unaware of what our body is telling the world, then no one else can know us. Even our future is predictable if we do not make changes in our thinking patterns. Truly, our bodies are walking billboards advertising everything there is to know about the *self* that we have created. You can know about most people's childhood experiences by looking at their lives and bodies now if they believed they were the events that happened to them. For example, two brothers grow up in the same home located in a ghetto. Both experience poverty, verbal abuse and neglect. One decides that he is not what happened to him and he becomes a minister. The other decides that he is what happened to him and he chooses crime. Our childhood experiences, viewed through our child eyes, caused us to develop an imagined reality of what life was like for us then.

On the contrary, a person who has developed their sense of awareness and understands how the body functions can understand everything there is to know about themselves and others. Even when they have covered themselves with the "armor" of suppressed feelings and emotions, the aware person can see the ill effects they have created in their body and can decide to "let go." Our physical and emotional diseases occurred as a result of forgetting who we are.

We marvel at psychics and pay them money to tell us what we already know about ourselves. We ask them to foretell our futures, as if it were a mystical secret, while our bodies are boldly projecting, down to the finest details, our spirits, our beliefs, our lifestyles, and how our minds and brains operate. The body, you see, is not a separate entity or a separate part of your mind and spirit.

The key to finding happiness in your life is achieved through living a life in synchronicity with your spirit and essence. It is called living on purpose. This involves living in harmony with your inner being and your external world. Finding balance in the spiritual world and the physical world lies in the ability to know what your body is telling you. Your purpose or intention represents your deeper spiritual purpose and is reflected in every aspect of your life, including your vocation. You hold your purpose or intention at the center of your lower belly.

The white light entering the crown of your head was already discussed in the Principle of Energy. Here's a repeat of the information on how to see this light. If you stand in front of a mirror and have a light, preferably off-white colored wall behind you, you can see that you possess an incredible funnel over the crown point of your head about one-third inch wide at the bottom. This is the way information from the universe enters. After spending time doing self-reflection you may have received intuitive information. The body has what I describe as a lightning rod going down its center. It has three important points. This is the first point of your lightning rod.

The second point of the lightning rod holds our spiritual longing. A person who has passion for life and for their life's work is aware of this place, also referred to as the soul seat. From the soul seat, diffused light beams in all directions.

People who cut off the awareness of their soul seat cloud it with a haze of dark energy. The result is a person out of touch with their present and future feelings. The posture of the body responds with a sunken chest that refuses to breathe the breath of life. Those who are still seeking their passion in life do not yet have beautiful diffused light extending from them. Their light is dimmed by the challenges they have placed in their lives such as illness, troubled relationships, and worries.

The center of your will to live in the physical world is the third point on the lightning rod. It is located two and one-half inches below the navel. When you are most powerful, it is like a gold ball.

What happens when we are off balance? Our body weight is mostly composed of our muscles. They use most of our body fuel. An off-balanced body has poor body posture, so it consumes greater amounts of energy just to hold itself up. When our muscles are working hard to hold up our skeletal structure, the nervous system is being affected. The result is that we have a greater amount of "chatter" in our internal field (our minds) and in our electromagnetic field. Our "chatter," also called our internal dialogue becomes noisy, and our electromagnetic field becomes cloudy. What is your internal dialogue?

Our minds are never idle. You can awaken from a deep sleep and know what you have been thinking. The question is what is the pattern of your thinking? Are you listening to a *committee of idiots*? You have the ability to direct your mind energy.

The second question is "How does the internal dialogue of the mind function?" The nerves are dictated to by the cortex, which receives thought in the form of suggestion from sight, sound, or any combination of the senses. The cortex then transforms the idea of feeling into bodily action. Sometimes it is harmful, sometimes helpful, depending upon attitude and the degree of stress associated with the thought.

We can learn how to intervene into our body's internal conversation. We take control of biochemical interactions through meditation, self-talk, prayer, and directed mind energy to return to a state of homeostasis. When emotions are expressed, we produce the bio-chemicals that are reflective of our emotions and our energies are kept flowing freely. When stored or blocked emotions are released through touch or other physical methods, there is a clearing of our internal pathways, which we experience as energy. When emotions are repressed, denied, not allowed to be whatever they may be, our network pathways get blocked, stopping the flow of the vital feel-good, unifying chemicals that run both our biology and our behavior.

Our bodies reflect our beliefs. People who are bowed forward lack faith in their Creator to provide for them and they lack confidence in themselves. They hunch over as if they are carrying a bag of rocks on their backs. When we get rigid in our thinking, believing that our ways are always right, being judgmental and self-absorbed, we restrain our feelings toward others. It is not possible to have feelings of love when you have shut off feelings of pain.

Things go awry for the person who acts in opposition to his intentions, who has not gone within to discover his life's purpose. Illness or emotional problems can result.

We can keep no secrets about our intentions because our intentions create the energy in our auric field. The color of the light a person is sending out is shown in the person's electro-magnetic field. For example, a person holding in the anger will have a dark deep red color in their electromagnetic field, even if they say they are not angry. Anger causes constriction of facial and body muscles. We've all seen a very angry person barely able to open their locked jaw. Others become so angry their bodies shake or tremble.

Ever described yourself as being off balanced, out of kilter? A person's physical body reflects dysfunction in his lightning/balancing rod. The misplacement of our intentionality causes the lightning/balancing rod to be either too far to the right or left, or too far backward or forward. A person with a healthy lightning/balancing rod, who stays on target with their intentions, reflects a spirit-mind-body that is straight, balanced, and energized. He is able to exist in the spiritual world and in the earthly world. Every aspect of his life is synchronized with his intention.

Persons experiencing chronic back problems push their pelvis forward, as if they are trying to push life. A person tilting the lower pelvis too far back is withholding from life. Announcers always refer to

Olympic winner Michael Johnson's unique running style. Actually, what he is doing is holding his body the way we all should be doing. He runs with perfect posture, which allows his lungs to take in the maximum amount of air. It allows him to be in perfect balance and alignment. His head sits erect on his shoulders so that his eyes are in perfect focus of the goal line. When he is interviewed after winning a race, you know through his words, his facial expression, everything about him that Michael Johnson knows the oneness of his spirit-mind-body.

How do you keep your lightning rod in alignment? The first point, located above the head, is where we have a very strong connection with the Creator. Techniques, such as self-reflection, chanting, or focused attention on an object, such as a flower, for fifteen or twenty minutes can help us get "still" and quiet the chatter in our minds and bodies so that we achieve a blissful state of being. This blissful state allows energy to circulate simultaneously through every mind-body cell.

Frederick Marthias Alexander, an Australian actor born in 1869, developed his educational approach while curing himself from a disconcerting loss of voice. The Alexander Technique focused attention on the relations between the head and the body. The head typically moves up from the top of the spine, and the back lengthens to relieve abnormal pressures upon it. The Alexander technique teaches that body alignment can be improved through awareness, control and self-awareness development. The Alexander Technique promotes both excitatory and inhibitory self-control, self-awareness, and spontaneity, mastery through surrender, and a rewarding sense of lightness and freedom.

Edmund Jacobson, an American physician found that relaxation of our skeletal muscles helps us to control our emotions. His technique of Progressive Relaxation activates the emotions and corrects the lack of alignment and balance of the second level of the lightning/balancing rod. People who vibrate at a higher level have both emotional and physical calmness and control. Their peace and harmony is reflected in their faces and bodies. Jacobson found that when our creations are in alignment with our Creator's, we create new sensorimotor skills and extraordinary states of awareness through the creation of balance in our spirit-mind-body.

The Functioning of the Mind-Body-Spirit

It was hard to decide how to discuss energy in its various forms—heat, magnetism, electrical energy, mental energy vibration, love, thoughts, and flow—and still remind the reader that we are still talking about energy. It is still harder for us to understand that we are not a body that has a separate spirit and mind, or that we are not mind-body with a spirit floating out in the somewhere. People say they know intellectually that spirit-body-mind are one, but they still believe that they can be spiritually disconnected and misaligned with their purpose. They think that it won't affect them mentally and physically. And it is not just the wholeness of the spirit-mind-body of one person we're talking about here. We're talking about each person being a part of the whole of the Universe.

The dilemma of the discussion becomes more problematic when we separate energy, light, and vibration into areas, and yet these areas are necessary to discuss each in detail and clarity. Hopefully as we "pull everything apart" to discuss the aspects, then we can "pull everything back" into wholeness.

Ask most people what they are made of, and they will reply, skin, hair, bones, muscles—body stuff—all the stuff that can change. **What we are really made of is energy. We are pure energy.** To discuss the oneness of spirit-mind-body we need to focus on the characteristics of that energy: connection, alignment, balance, harmony, love, and light.

Mind Energy

Our minds create habitual patterns of thinking which will determine the experiences of our life.

We use mind energy to:
Open us up to receive the knowledge of intuition
Create psychosomatic and psychogenic diseases or keep our bodies in a state of homeostasis—balance, harmony, and peace.
Heal our body
Choose the thoughts that create our emotions
Determine our level of stress, fear and doubts.
Raise or lower our blood pressure and cholesterol
Create a healthy or dysfunctional sex life
Create energy, enable us to relax, heighten our perception
Activate our immune system or cause our immune system to act against your body
Release serotonin that helps us sleep
Create emotional states that can help us be more successful, powerful and in control

Enhance our creativity, reinforce our willpower
Create centeredness
And most importantly...Connect us to the Creator

Recent Discoveries about the Brain

The news on September 1, 1999 reported that researchers can change the genetics of mice to make them smarter. The report also said that in the near future they would be able to help children with learning difficulties. The really important information is that we are already able to increase the pathways of our neural cells. Pathways are increased through exercise of our bodies and our minds. Our brains never stop growing and changing.

The end result of our either controlling our brains and our stored memories is that our actions determine whether we succeed or fail in our professions, relationships, goals and purpose. Remember, actions are manifestations of mind energy, emotional energy, physical energy, and spiritual energy. We can't fail to project who we are. And this projection is the result of our looking inward and then sending out what we found. So whatever you are seeking you will find.

Now you need to think about this next statement. "What you accept from the world outside, you do so because you wanted it first and accepted as true." So whatever success or failure you want, only you have the ability to manifest it. Many times we will protest that we do not want failure, but if is still happening to us, it is a definite sign that we still want it.

"The mind is only able to be aware of the things of its own contents." For example, we all know that we are taught self-limiting fears. We make choices about the incoming information in the form of sensations that we receive because the mind can distort that information. For instance, an anorexic young woman can see the bones sticking out of her body and still think that she is overweight. Or, if someone is critical of you and you get offended. If you didn't believe that there was some validity to the criticism, you wouldn't have reacted to it.

Two people could receive stimulation from the same experience and through identical sensory devices, but still process and interpret the information differently and thus respond differently. What is it that we can do when we choose to use our minds? The answer is EVERYTHING!

Here are some examples of what people are able to do:

1. Under extreme stress, Sir Thomas Moore and Marie Antoinette turned their hair white in a few seconds.

2. Manic-depressives who suffer from psoriasis often get worse when they are depressed. The psoriasis clears up when they are manic.

3. Blisters "weep" more when a patient is sad than when the person is happy.

4. Even the modest stress of having to do mental arithmetic changes the electrical resistance of the skin.

5. Rosacea, reddening of the face, is interpreted as a disturbance of the normal mechanism of blushing, due to a guilty conscience.

6. Resentment and aggression are held to lie behind the itchy condition known as urticaria.

7. A woman who was allergic to roses reacted as usual when artificial roses were placed in the room.

8. Hysterical blindness is caused when inhibitory circuits or substances in the brain simply block the visual circuits. Some soldiers unable to cope with the horrors of war experience hysterical blindness.

9. Hysterical paralysis occurs when powerful emotions generate inhibition of basic sensory and motor pathways.

10. Glove anesthesia is when the hand becomes insensitive following some painful episode.

11. A Dutch psychiatrist related how all the symptoms of a severe cold vanished shortly before he was to deliver an important scientific paper and came back again soon after the job was done.

12. Syndrome shift is the replacement of one set of disease manifestations by another. If a disease is produced by an unconscious conflict, curing the disease merely forces the unconscious to find another.

13. A Catholic who was seriously ill with heart disease was visited by a priest. Apparently convinced that the priest had come to administer the last rites, the patient was so scared that he suffered a heart attack and died.

14. Stigmata is marks on hands and feet resembling the wound received by Christ. Less often, bleeding from the head or side has been reported. A doctor once had a case where blood appeared on Thursday, appeared in spurts on Friday and vanished on Sunday.

15. A religious 10 year-old black girl began to bleed from her left palm. Blood seeped from her palm 4 to 6 times daily during Easter week. She bled from her right palm, then the bottom of her left foot, her right thorax and finally the middle of her head.

16. Hypnosis can cure asthma and skin diseases. Swelling can be reduced, bleeding stopped and even gangrene arrested.

These bodily responses to mental states are mediated through the hypothalamus and through the sympathetic and parasympathetic nervous systems. The sympathetic nervous system is an automatic system whose activities are normally unconscious, though **it has recently been shown that these autonomic functions can be brought under conscious control.** We can consciously slow down our heartbeat, we can stop our headaches, and we can control our pain. The body reacts to emotions of which we are not conscious. We have an upset stomach and we don't connect it to having a confrontation. We react *as if* we felt anxiety, even when we think anxiety is repressed—until we look down at our sweaty hands.

Most of our day is spent using cognitive think-ing. It enables us to observe our nervousness and analyze the cause and then to decide our course of action. It is using our whole brain, first on the right side seeing imagery or knowing intuitively, and then using the left side to analyze the information. Cognition is various ways of knowing—analysis and reasoning, pattern recognition through the use of metaphor, intuitive comprehension of another person's subjective state, problem solving that involves visual, auditory or other imagery, and mystical illumination.

It is important for us to understand that our bodies are receiving and transmitting stations for mind energy. Much of the information we receive in cognitive thinking comes from outside of our selves. Other mind energy that we receive is described as intuitive, in the form of a small still voice, or as a sense of knowing. The important thing is that we have the ability to reject or receive information, we can interpret it, and we can use our minds to assimilate information.

Two things, our belief system and our sensory perceptions, however, alter our sense of knowing. The belief system is formed from past memories and experiences and held in the subconscious mind, which then affects the thoughts in the conscious mind. It is important that we constantly monitor our belief system and ask, "what happened to me so that I hold on to this belief?" The second is our interpretation of incoming data based on our five senses. When we make a decision, express a belief, or begin to act, we need to ask ourselves, is it based on my belief system or some false incoming data. Upon what am I basing my decision? For example, what if you met a woman who wore the same perfume your ex-wife did? Would you still hold anger toward the new woman and would you have a correct perception of the new woman?

So we have just described our minds as being in constant state of movement, that is constantly thinking something, some of which is subject to being falsely transmitted. That enlivened energy moves continuously through our body by the electrical transmission of our cells—brain, blood, and nerve cells. Mind energy also moves through these same cells through chemical production of our glands and neurotransmitters.

Think of the perfect television station transmitting pure signals to all of the television sets (humans) in the world. Each station has the ability to transmit the mind energy in unaltered form if it is totally "clear" of inside interference. But our own internal dialogue, created by our false sense impressions and belief system, distorts the original message. For example, we've seen people with such poor self-worth that they distort almost everything said to them.

Just as our connection to the world via the Internet enables us to be a receiving station, we have at any moment access to all of the answers to our challenges, when we connect to universal energy. There is not one question that we can ask whose answer isn't based on a universal truth. All answers are available; we only need to ask. Look at it this way, everything that we need to make future discoveries is already there. Marconi didn't have to invent the airwaves to invent the radio; he just had to learn how to use them. He took the universe's principles—formation is transmitted by airwaves. Do you get the connection that our thoughts are electrical, and they do not stop at the confines of our body? They project outward just like a radio transmitter and enable our minds to create, heal, and project positive thought infinitely.

We only think our physical body imposes limitations on our ability to see, hear, and speak. Mind energy, transmitted through your spirit-mind-body, is capable of doing each of these things without physical sight, auditory hearing and vibratory speech. **We can envision places we have never seen, hear sounds that we have never heard, and transmit words without auditory sounds. It simply a matter of our being attuned to these abilities.** As children we were given "standardized tests" on what information we were to have learned through rote memorization. We should have been taught how to open our minds to receive the thoughts of the universal mind. Receiving intuitive information didn't have to be limited to Bach, Emerson, and the Greek philosophers; they were just open to receive it.

We are a molecule of energy in the universal mind system. Our choice is at what level we wish to participate. When we do not still our minds and bodies, when we place judgments on the incoming sensory interpretation, and when we act upon past thinking processes, we lock out the universe's mind energy. Devices can measure our brain activity because brain-waves reflect fluctuations of energy. An EEG graph shows that neurons experience electrical activity. When you flat line, you are considered physically dead. During our normal conscious state, when we are more aware of the external world than our internal world, we experience small rapid brainwaves called beta rhythms. During relaxation, meditation and self-reflection our brainwaves in the alpha and theta states are larger and slower. In altered states of consciousness, our brain waves shift into an even higher level of organization.

Mind energy includes the energy of our conscious awareness and our subconscious self. The thoughts and emotions we are aware and unaware of affect our health, success, actually everything about us. Two other things to remember about mind energy: the mind's energy and the body's energy system interact in very specific ways and willpower, that thing which directs life energy through our bodies, is centered in the mind. The power of decision is the one thing that gives us freedom. You can decide to see things right or to see things incorrectly.

Mind energy carries information that can be directed through concentration to a specific part of the body. This is how we slow down our blood flow, control pain, even during childbirth, or destroy a cancerous tumor. We can use our mental energy to control the direction of energy flowing in and out of channels, plus, the exact form the flow of energy will take. Hypnotized patients can actually produce voltage changes in specific parts of the body.

Our self-healing spirit-mind-body is always seeking homeostasis. We can remember how it felt to be healthy, full of energy, and it is up to us to use our internal resources to return to this healthy energetic state. Try an experiment. Ask a person who is in a relaxed state to bring to mind a major concern in their life. . Ask them to say a phrase or word about it and then watch their body "shift" and react to what they are thinking. You can get a sense what they are feeling as their brain waves shift. When we speak a mantra, write or read poetry, or call upon our imaginations, we are uniting our brain. Transformation occurs in the mind and the body. You can watch the person's eyes and their bodies reveal the "ah-ha" moment.

The level of consciousness or our awareness through our senses—sight, touch, taste, smell and feel—and our awareness through intuition (direct knowing), enables us to be energetic or non-energetic, healthy or unhealthy. It is important to change our paradigm that pain is bad and should be repressed. Pain is good because it alerts us that we are not connected, balanced, aligned, or in a word, healthy. The more aware our state of consciousness, the more accurate our perceptions, the more we see life as a growth opportunity filled with unlimited choices, yet with opportunities to make discriminations and be selective in all areas of life.

Let's use the Internet again as a model to understand the concept of our being energy, light, and love. The Internet in this case is like the one primal energy—infinite mind, God energy, Supreme Intelligence, Love, or the Source.

In this scenario we are represented as computers because we have the same characteristics—we operate as energy and we send information via energy. The physical computer is just "housing" or a "receiving transformer" for energy. We are connected via energy to the Source and to all the other transformers. We are by nature "plugged into" universal energy.

We can choose whether we are *open,* that is, receiving all the information that is sent to us. For example, we all have hard drives like our computers. We operate on the principle of receiving information via our five physical senses and the sixth sense, intuition. Each of us has additional programs added as time goes on. In humans we call it experiences. We may have the same software as others, but our experiences are "written in" according to what has happened to us specifically. Like people, no two computers contain the same information.

Seven major metabolic vortexes in our bodies receive and send energy. From the top of the body down, they are located at major organs: hypothalamus, pineal, thyroid, heart, pancreas, kidneys, and gonads. I prefer to call them the "stars" in our bodies. Our body's stars are either open or closed depending upon how clogged or free they are as energy receivers. A weak, depleted star is incapable of gathering the information, therefore, the picture it is receiving, "reality," is fuzzy and distorted. Just as your computer is nothing without its energy source, your spirit-mind-body is not "whole" or "holy" without its energy source. The seven stars will be discussed in The Principle of Flow.

Now, let's look at the information you are sending out via E-mail. For the other person to receive your E-mail, you must be on the same "wave length." For instance, you may be on one Internet server and your friend is on another Internet server. The two servers have to make arrangements to be of the same mindset and wavelength. Like E-mail, once the message is sent out, it goes on forever.

Returning to the computer comparison helps us see the mind as able to transmit beyond the confines of time and space. Look at the example of when a lot of computers are networked. You can sit in Atlanta and make a change that appears simultaneously on all the computers that are networked. This is beyond time and space. Information can be sent anywhere instantly. We are always being told that we can't change other people. Not true. Why else would advertisers spend millions of dollars?

In the same way, our bodies, through their nerve channels, operates in electrical (energy) waves sending out information in radiating circles infinitely. We have listened far too long to people who want to control us by telling us we are powerless and without potential. When we become embodiers and manifesters through our thoughts, we discover how to express and how to utilize them.

Your thought-images are always being impressed upon yourself and others. **The quality of your thoughts—negative or positive—are consciously or unconsciously activated into every nerve, muscle and tissue of your body.** You can make other people feel good by sending them good thoughts. We can literally change their state. Scientific studies have shown that people prayed for, no matter how far away, heal faster. We must replace negative thought energy with positive thought energy. Just as your computer is nothing without its energy source, your mind-body-spirit is not "whole" or "holy" without its energy source.

Separating the discussion of the body in order to discuss the way the body functions in no way means that it functions apart from the spirit-mind. So as you read the following, very necessary material to the understanding of Energy Management, I hope that you will keep in mind the Oneness of Spirit-Mind-Body.

How Light Affects Our Glands

We have three glands in our head that function primarily because of the light (energy) taken in through the eyes. But before we begin to discuss the hypothalamus, the pituitary and the pineal glands, we need to discuss how the eyes operate and how they are connected to these three glands.

We use our eyes for more than just seeing what is in front of us. The amount of light that we permit to enter indicates our general and emotional health. The more open we are to new information and the more we practice new ways of thinking the more we are opening our eyes, our vision, to our creation possibilities.

The Hypothalamus

Activities of the hypothalamus and the effects of our emotions:

It controls the adrenal glands and the pituitary gland. It regulates the appetite and monitors the level of blood sugar in the body. Note here the connection here of how our emotions cause us to want to eat more or less.

It acts as the body's thermostat, regulating temperature control, and is a prime switching center for signals destined for functions controlled by the autonomic nervous system, such as, the operating muscles of the heart and lungs, and the digestive and circulatory systems.

You are nothing without the hypothalamus because this is where physical and emotional energy begins in the body. The hypothalamus initiates the stress response and sends out immune functions. The hypothalamus is a drug factory. It manufactures and secretes stress-sensitive hormones that unleash a torrent of other body chemicals-epinephrine, norepinephrine, and corticosteroids- known to have definite effects on the immune system.

The region of the hypothalamus coordinates a phenomenal portion of the body's activity. It transmits and receives signals all over the nervous system and hormonally through the bloodstream. Remember, the nervous system takes in information through our five physical senses: seeing, hearing, smelling, touch, feeling, and the sixth sense, intuition. Everything that we perceive about our external world is relayed through these senses.

The body's homeostatic center for health, balance and harmony, the hypothalamus, is important because of its broad sphere of influences. It is a small cluster of brain tissue barely larger than a thumb tip weighing about a quarter of an ounce. Situated deep inside the lower midsection of the brain, it acts as a busy neural interchange.

The hypothalamus is the site of the body's pacemaker and biological clock, and is thought to regulate a number of bodily functions such as: ***reproduction, thirst, hunger, satiation, temperature, and sleep patterns.*** In addition to all of these activities that involve the use of energy, the hypothalamus also regulates our emotions. The wide variety of our emotions is both chemically and electrically charged.

How Light from the Sun, the Stars, and People Goes to Every Cell

Light from the sun, stars, and even artificial light enters the eye and goes to the body's **power distribution center**, the hypothalamus, where it is converted into **electrochemical impulses** (energy) that are sent to the pituitary and the pineal, two important endocrine glands. We also receive light from the earth's electromagnetic field and from the electromagnetic field of people. **These glands, in turn, distribute the hormonal messages via the body's nervous system to virtually every cell in the body. Again, the "connections" must be emphasized.**

We don't actually see light or different colors with our eyes. In the human eye, one photon (a wave of energy) gives up its energy to the retina, which somehow converts it into the electrical signal that **produces**

the sensation of light. Those with higher frequencies have more energy than those with lower frequencies.

Ever said, "I'm so mad I see red!" Well, red, especially the darker shades of red, is the lowest of the light frequencies. When you are angry, you are giving all your attention to the low frequency of negativity, thereby depleting your energy by sending it to another person or object. The level of self is then at its lowest form.

Remember this information when you read the benefits of Stillness and Self-Reflection. When we sit quietly and stop the chatter going on in our minds, we are able to raise our level of vibration. We actually feel lighter because we are allowing light from the universe to enter our bodies—no matter where we are. We are then able to direct this light wherever it is needed, wherever the body has a sense of dis-ease.

This information should give us an **insight** (sight within) into why it is so important that we spend time outdoors letting sunlight enter our eyes. Those who spend all their time working under fluorescent lights, lights which are not full spectrum lighting, or in front of the TV, are subject to creating depression.

The Pituitary Gland

The pituitary gland, called the "master gland," is controlled by the hypothalamus. Remember the hypothalamus converts the electrochemical impulses (light). The pituitary gland produces important chemicals that affect our bodies. Your happiness depends on this pea-sized gland connected to the base of the brain that releases the powerful brain drugs, the endorphins. Ever try to learn or remember something when you are tired or depressed? While they are **powerful painkill-**

ers, you will probably be most interested in knowing that endorphins help us to **learn and remember.** The endorphins circulate in the blood and lymph systems and attach to specific molecules, or receptor sites, located in the brain and other body parts. Endorphins are opiates manufactured by the brain. **Hypnotic therapy tends to release this morphine-like substance and brings about changes in breathing, depression, and alleviation of pain** as well as arthritis and other pain conditions.

We usually think of the pituitary gland as controlling our size, but it does so much more. The pituitary controls the activities of the other endocrine glands by the secretion of growth hormone, thyroid stimulation hormone TSH, ACTH, prolactin, luteinizing and follicle stimulation hormones (LH) and FSH, oxytocin, melanocyte stimulating hormone. The hypothalamus secretes a Neuro-hormone called corticotrophin-releasing factor (CFR), which activates the pituitary gland. Powerful chemicals rush out of the pituitary, among them a large master molecule called the pro-opiocortin. Along with this, the body produces other secretions; the most important of which in terms of stress is ACTH. It also travels to the adrenal glands via the bloodstream. The main idea to grasp is that it is not good to have too much or too little CRF or ACTH since they determine the working of our immune system.

The Pineal Gland

Remember the Biblical quotes "You are a light unto the world" and "Don't hide your light under a bushel." Ever been told to *let your light shine*? **The following is an explanation of how light enters the spirit-mind-body, how light affects the body, and how you can maximize your energy output using light.**

The pineal gland is a tiny pinecone-shaped structure in the center of the head. The pineal has been called a *body,* a *gland* and now is called an *organ.* It is called the **originator of thought. This is where we receive intuition, activate our imaginations and do our creative thinking.** It is through the pineal gland that we are connected to our Creator—higher energy, energy itself. The pineal is the location of the "third eye" and where we are connected to our Creator's Divine Mind. For this reason it is also called **the seat of the soul, and the seat of our consciousness.** When we meditate and self-reflect, we "open" ourselves to receive direct communication from universal spirit. On the physical level the pineal gland is called an intake organ and is discussed again in The Principle of Flow. It is the body's **"light meter;"** it is the body's regulator of regulators. **It regulates everything that is happening in the body, and it is the only part of our being that doesn't receive any information from any higher neurological centers.** Note that this gland, like the hypothalamus and the pituitary, functions according to the amount of light it receives.

The pineal receives information from the environment about light and darkness by way of the eyes; it also receives information about the earth's electromagnetic field. It is the part of our being that is receptive to information from the heavens above us and from the earth beneath our feet. The pineal gland is the connecting rod between the grounding forces and the universal energies. Remember the discussion about the lightning/balancing rod going down the center of our body?

The pineal is the part of our being that lays the basic foundation for relationship. It knows what is going on with us externally and internally. Everything in our life is a function of relationship. We have a relationship with our Creator, Divine Love. We have a relationship with our self, with others, and with everything in the universe.

The gland sends hormones (chemical energy) with information to every cell in the body. You will read how the hormones enter cells via neurotransmitters and changes them. Think a minute about how light and darkness affects you. During the darkest part of the winter months people become depressed because of the lack of light and suffer a disease call SAD. These people are encouraged to sit outdoors on sunshiny days. To a certain degree, we all suffer the "winter blahs."

Why is it important that we get enough light? Light enters the eye, affects the retina, then goes to the hypothalamus, and then the hypothalamus passes this information on to the pineal. **The pineal creates a very interesting hormone called melatonin, which is the only hormone in the body we know of that can do anything it wants, anytime it wants, anywhere it wants.** Melatonin is a very powerful hormone that comes into creation from the pineal's relationship with light and darkness. Melatonin secretion in humans can be changed at will by exposure to steady magnetic fields of the same strength as the geomagnetic field.

This is the reason you should not turn on the light when you get up at night. We know that sleeping problems stem from being out of sync.

Like the other two glands, the pineal sends hormones with information **to every cell in the body.** Our individual cells use the information to direct their internal function and synchronize themselves with Mother Nature. When a person has a chronically abnormal biocycle, the result is a chronic stress syndrome, which causes the immune system to weaken.

Though the phrase is overused, still the eyes are the windows of the soul—they interrelate with light. The eyes are a reflection of the part of our mind that analyzes things. We call that **foveal vision,** or detail vision. **Peripheral vision** is the aspect of our vision that reflects the part of our being that feels the environment.

We don't actually *see* **with our eyes.** The eyes are sensors that take in light; another of these sensors is the skin. But the seeing doesn't happen within the eye, and it doesn't happen within the brain; yet, somehow it seems to happen everywhere at the same time. The following information is present to explain how this happens.

As you have read, the pineal gland has everything to do with the light entering our eyes. Sight is one of our five senses—and one of the means we use to develop a higher sense of consciousness. The information travels through the nervous system. The eyes contain 70% of the body's sense receptors. **It is through these receptors that we learn 90% of our information.** It is important to note that while both eyes are working together, we really have two views because there is a small difference between our eyes.

It is said that we actually have three different eyes, **the eye of the flesh,** the physical eye, **the eye of**

reason, the mental eye; and **the third eye,** the contemplative eye, the eye that "appreciates." As we noted earlier the third eye, through which we see real vision, is where we gain the ability to see the invisible. As the third eye (the inner eye) opens, we are able to see what at one time we felt was invisible. We tune into a broader spectrum, not only of the electromagnetic spectrum, but of subtle energies that are not even within this electromagnetic spectrum. A blind man appearing on The Hour of Power explained that for just a minute he was able to see his wife and daughter. I believe that he was able to see them using his third eye.

Our eyes are the most complex and intricate system in the universe, containing more than **1 billion parts**. Two million fibers from the eyes are connected to the brain. It is important to understand that they are actual extensions of the brain. An area about the size of the cortex controls the visual area. **Two thirds of the three billion messages relayed to the brain every second are sent from the eyes. One fourth of the brain is used to process what the eyes see.** As light enters the eye, it is transformed into electrical impulses by the photoreceptors. The electrical impulses are sent to the brain at approximately 234 miles per hour. The entire brain is involved in sending the impulses along different routes. **Some travel to the visual cortex for the construction of images, while others travel to the brain's hypothalamus, our body's homeostatic center, and affect our vital functions.** Together, the eyes and brain represent only 2% of our body weight. Yet they require 25% of the nutritional intake. The eyes alone require one-third as much oxygen as the heart, high intake of vitamin C, and have the highest need of zinc (our intelligence chemical). Does this make you want to be more conscious of the foods you are eating?

Light affects the 137 million photoreceptors in each eye (130 million are called rods and 7 million are called cones.) We use the lower numbered cones during daylight for visual acuity and color discrimination. It requires the higher numbered rods that function in twilight to operate during colorless vision and movement at low levels of illumination.

Take out a mirror and look at your eye. Focus on the iris, the colored part of your eye. Everything in nature has a perfect plan. The beautiful colors of flowers were created to attract the insects that feed from them and then pollinate other plants. The color of your eye also was no accident. Because our eyes are different colors, our brains are affected differently. Light entering our colored eyes is affecting different areas of our brain. Iridologists use sensitive video cameras to analyze abnormal tissue conditions, inflammations, and toxic organs and tissues in the body. Remember to look at what your eyes reveal about your health the next time you have a cold. Studies have shown that 66% of the people suffering from depression, schizophrenia, or alcoholism have visual problems.

The following are examples of how our brains are also affected by the colors we view. For example, weight lifters are not as powerful when they view a pink wall, and out of control prisoners placed in a bubble gum pink room are calmed down. On the other hand, red makes us feel more aggressive. Yellow not only brightens our disposition, but a yellow piece of paper placed on the desk of children with learning difficulties has been proven to increase their learning abilities. When people are thinking they exude yellow light.

Important Parts of the Brain

The **Corpus Callosum** houses a mass of nerve fibers that act as conductors carrying messages from the right side to the left of the brain. The three glands you just read about send chemicals (hormones) through the nervous system. The **neurons** in the nervous system are the chemical transmitters of messages from the brain to all over the body. Everything is controlled, from the heartbeat and motor abilities to sensory perception and emotional responses.

Thoughts and emotions are then transmitted to the cerebral cortex of the brain, where the information is sorted out. The cerebral cortex is the brain's analyzer, acting as a receiving station for information fed to it by the nervous system. There are billions of interconnecting nerves that act together to produce individual habit patterns. These nerves are dictated to by the cortex, which receives thought in the form of suggestion from sight, sound, or any combination of the senses. **The cortex then transforms the idea of feeling into bodily action.** Sometimes it is harmful, sometimes helpful, depending upon attitude and the degree of stress associated with the thought. When stress or troubled emotions accompany a thought to the cortex, the resulting tension interferes with the positive functioning of this part of your brain. We reinforce the habit of reacting nervously. For example, we might distract a crying child with a loud noise or a laugh. The result was that the child stopped crying because his thought and reaction process was interrupted.

Sensations are flashed from the nervous system to the brain, and **immediately** a reaction takes place in some part of the anatomy. Over 500 muscles are attached to various parts of the body. When a muscle receives a message from the brain, the muscle impulsively shortens and contracts, thereby causing pressure on the nerves that pass through it. **Should there be no release of this contraction, the excess tension remains in the muscles surrounding the nerve fibers.** This prolonged contraction is at the base of nervousness. This book will go into greater detail later about the way muscles function, but the point to be stressed here again is that **thought is energy carried through our nervous system.** Therapists refer to this condition as "residual tension." Unresolved areas of tension within the body eventually lead to the breakdown of healthy functioning, and thus are the forerunners of disease. Some tension is good, it lets you know you are alive. But if you are tense most of the time, and living under pressure all the time, your nervous system will be overwhelmed.

The Body's Production of Physical Energy

We know that the body produces infrared heat. The beginning of the book discussed how we as magnetic beings attract or repel different energies. Our bodies function from electrical energy sent through the nervous system and chemical energy sent through hormones and other chemicals. A body with a high energy level is healthy, active, feels lighter and is more productive.

The sensitivity of our eyes, ears, hands and skin allows them to receive much of our sensory input. It would be worth your time to look at your nervous system in an anatomy book focusing on your head, hands, and feet. We have several nerves close to our ears that enable us to receive sensory input. The hands are full of nerves. Each finger has a nerve running on either side of the bone. This is the reason our hands send out so much energy. The buccinator and buccal are branches of facial nerves spread out around the jaw-bones that send and receive energy from the brain. Remember how exhausted you feel after you have wasted your energy being angry. Watch a nervous or an angry person's face twitch when he tries to constrain energy. They look and feel like they are going explode because they are holding on to so much negative energy. What we have been "holding on to" shows in our faces. You can look at a hardened criminal's sardonic grin and know their history. A life filled with despair produces a turned down mouth just as a compulsive person develops a stiff upper lip.

Every cell contributes to sending and receiving of heat, magnetic energy, chemical energy and electrical energy. Each cell in our body has a specific function, and each cell can duplicate the work of the whole organ. One live muscle cell of the heart seen under a microscope will individually continue to beat. Another live muscle cell placed under the microscope will also beat, but at a different rate. When the two cells are placed next to each other, they will beat at the same rate. Energy within each cell causes them to continue beating. The cells demonstrate that they have memory, energy, and are holographic. They also demonstrate that they "talk" and work together through connection.

This "talk" is mind energy. It is through mind energy that we can heal our bodies on an individual cell basis. Cells that are growing out of control, such as cancer cells, can be directed to die with mind energy. You might want to pay attention to the last sentence since two out of three people will have some form of cancer during their lifetime.

Have you ever wondered what makes the million sperm released during sex swim to a woman's egg? How does the sperm know which direction to go? Mind energy and electrical energy in each sperm propels it to try to enter the egg. Both the egg and the sperm are vibrating and causing the attraction. A fertilized egg is a perfect example of balance because is composed of 23 chromosomes from the male and 23 chromosomes from the female. Even at this point, the egg contains everything that it needs. Just in the first week, the egg grows 10,000 percent.

Spirit-Mind-Body Programming

Knowing the *how* our spirit-mind-body has been programmed from birth up to this point helps us understand why we are high energy or depleted energy, successful or unsuccessful, and emotionally alive or dead. People who have high energy, who are in control of their lives and live in balance and harmony, have adjusted and changed their programming from external influences to internal influences. They have stopped responding to external influences.

Our programming began as children and continues to expand and change by the way we choose to react to our experiences. Four ideas to remember are:

1. As long as our programming creates our beliefs, we let our programming determine our beliefs.
2. Our beliefs determine our attitudes. A belief is a strong emotional state of certainty that you hold about specific people, things, or experiences in life.
3. Our attitudes, the results of reactions, create our feelings.
4. Our feelings determine our actions.

Improved Success Means Changing Your Belief Systems

It is an absolute fact that everything you think, do and experience is based on your belief system. In order to be more successful in business and in your personal life, you must take an inventory of what you believe about yourself.

You began creating your belief system as a child, and unfortunately for many of us, we have based our belief system on the experiences and events which happened in our lives. Successful people know that these two things are not *who they are* and that they are responsible for creating the kind of world in which they want to live. In other words, they have chosen where they wanted to direct their energies.

Most often we have based our belief system on conceptions and misconceptions rather than truth. The reason many salespeople fail, for example, is because they think, down deep, that they are not good enough to be successful or they don't deserve success. This thinking taints all their efforts and causes them to operate from patterned thinking of self-sabotage. Dr. Robert Schuller tells us, "We must first change our inward perception in order to change our outer actions."

Want to change your success? You need to know how to control your conscious and subconscious thinking. Reading about how the brain works is not the most interesting subject, but it will definitely change your life.

Hopefully, we can now see how our different programming influences the information that we receive. We are all receiving the same information about the next electronic discovery, but most of us will not connect with it because our focus and programming are not tuned in. For this reason, we must stay open about how we can utilize the mind energy flowing through us. We want to continually be open to new programs by refusing patterned thinking. This is the way that we "spark" new ideas. **Opening new programs actually causes increased electrical activity in our minds.**

How Your Brain Works

* Your thoughts and your reaction to experiences constantly change your spirit-mind-body. "As a man thinketh, so is he."
* You can choose the habitual patterns in which your brain works.
* Our brain has one million, million brain cells that act as a micro-data base for all incoming information. It does not make judgment calls.
* The cells of your brain (neurons) produce electro-chemical charge through thousands of tentacles that come from the axon and nucleus of the cell.
* Each tentacle has bumps called spines and synaptic buttons that contain chemicals. Thoughts produce electrical charges (energy) which are transmitted through the tentacles. The spines and buttons are

linked to others by electrical impulses carrying chemicals.

Each tentacle is like the branch of a tree, radiating from the cell center or nucleus. The branches of the brain cell are called dendrites. One particularly large and long branch, called the axon, is the main exit for information transmitted by that cell. Fluids travel through the axon.

On the dendrites are little mushroom-like protuberances called dendritic spines and synaptic buttons. Each dendrite spine/synaptic button contains bundles of chemicals that are the major message-carriers in our human thinking process. Now do you know why we tell people to quit pushing our buttons?

A dendritic spine/synaptic button from one brain cell will link with a synaptic button from another brain cell. When an electrical impulse travels through the brain cell, chemicals will be transferred across the minute, liquid-filled space between the two. The space is called the synaptic gap.

* In each human brain there are an estimated one million, million brain cells. One cell (neuron) would fit on the head of a pin.
* Each of these cells works as a huge electrochemical complex.
* Each cell works as a powerful micro-data processing and transmitting system.

That brain of yours is the most powerful computer in the world because it receives thousands of incoming impulses every second, which it directs to the appropriate route. Biochemical electromagnetic pathways are formed from each message, thought or memory. ***You can control your thinking by reframing and***

creating new pathways. First, change your attitude or perception of your memories. Second, choose the thoughts and messages you have, and thirdly, choose whether you apply emotion. Emotionally charged thinking has more power because emotional states create chemical changes in the brain.

We have been inaccurately taught that we can't control our thinking. ***Want to change your patterned negative thinking?*** First, you must realize that your past thoughts are stored in data memories. Memories are also patterns of behavior and thought. More importantly, memories don't just sit around; they are ***dissipative energy structures.*** When the energy of a memory is activated, it sets off ripples throughout our bodies creating new connections. To create a new thought pattern, you may encounter some biochemical/electromagnetic resistance the first time you present it. Remember that we are describing these thoughts as Electro (energy) and magnetic (coming together). So the next time you think a similar thought, it becomes easier. Repetition changes habits and beliefs. Add charged emotion, and you will move more rapidly. Old patterns change when maximally perturbed. Look at the dramatic effects—healings, release of phobias and traumatic events—that happen to people during meditation, hypnosis, or guided imagery. Old paradigms and beliefs, compulsive behaviors, all the things we think we are "stuck in" are really just places where we have chosen to put our energies and can quickly be changed.

You have the ability to change your mind about an event in your past because you can change your perception. Actually, the past is unreal and it enables you to let it go. The past is the thoughts and energy stored in your mind.

Our futures are unreal also. There is only the present moment. Our power point is now, each moment, this instant in time. Trying to stay in our past or project into the future robs you of your power and energy.

Mental imagery is a transformative technique used in psychotherapy. In conjunction with cartharsis, focused intention, and the acceptance (or reowning) of dissociated functioning, such imagery facilitates healing and growth by helping to restructure ruling attitudes, by providing access to repressed or previously unnoticed psychological processes, by helping to modify perception, by facilitating skill rehearsal, and by mediating awareness of bodily structure.

Imagery is a form of therapy based on the use of directed meditation or hypnosis. It uses all the senses to experience. Such experience can be visual, auditory, tactile, kinesthetic, gustatory, or olfactory, with faint or vivid, noticed or unnoticed, and easy or difficult to apprehend.

When imagery is used in healing, the subject first achieves a state of relaxation and is then guided by the therapist through an imaginary experience. The mental images may depict the disease cells as villains, etc. The therapist assists the patient in picturing in his or her mind an image that, if held, will lead to a physical healing.

The cultivation of imagery facilitates new sensorimotor skills of extraordinary states of consciousness by recruitment of countless psychological and somatic processes. By means of such recruitment, countless cells, all of them interlocked in the service of homeostasis, are led in tandem by mental images. Examples are the practice of different roles or sub-personalities, the repetition of healing affirmations, a sustained expectation of success, concentration, employment of kinesthetic awareness to modify autonomic functioning, deliberate recall of unnoticed or dissociated processes, focused intention, surrender to ego-transcending powers. Highly complex reactions in us can be triggered by transformative modalities.

Hypnotic suggestion and imagery practice can improve performance on visual memory tasks. Watch a person preparing to draw pull the memory of the item from their brain. Hypnotic suggestion and imagery practice also evoke comprehensive images for problem solving and reveal memories and perceptions that words do not adequately represent. All of these activities are done with the right side of our brain. This is where we promote the ability to restructure conceptual systems, and facilitate non-analytic, holistic strategies involved in creative inspiration. This is the reason that you cannot be creative by forcing yourself. You must *allow* your mind to *rest,* freeing the information to appear to you. Meditation and rituals we use in religious practices promote concentration and access to the mind's subliminal depths. By learning to *be still* we can stimulate mystical knowing. These disciplines strengthen mental capacities or improve the perceptual, emotional, and volitional processes they involve.

The best way to make changes is learning to create images in our minds. Imagery, as stated before, is defined as the cultivation of images that facilitate new sensorimotor skills of extraordinary states of consciousness by recruitment of countless psychological and somatic processes. Now what does that mean? We are able to create what we want by using our five senses to make what we desire to be real in our minds. If you want a sense of peace, you picture the most peaceful place you know, you hear the sounds of peace, you can breathe in sweet smells, and you feel softness all around you. To heal themselves, people picture the destruction of malignant cells, they feel being healthy, and they use healing music. Suggestive imagery is the reason pla-cebo effects and spiritual healing work. Sick people who use healing affirmations and have an expectation of success, who act as if they are well, who have faith in their physician, some kind of procedure, a religious figure or person they believe has healing powers, are more likely to be healed.

We are able to create imagery to use as mind energy to direct countless cells to do what we want. We do this by the practice of different roles or sub-personalities. People with multiple personalities may have one personality that suffers from a disease, while the other personality does not. One personality may need to wear glasses, while the others do not. You don't have to have multiple personalities to choose to be someone else at different times. Imagery helps our concentration and focused intention, plus, we can use it to help us deliberately recall unnoticed or dissociated processes. An eyewitness to a crime is put in a hypnotic state and then asked to pull up images of the event. Imagery enables us to surrender to the ego self; it gives us transcending powers to higher transformative states.

The more often you use your new enlightened, positive thinking, the clearer and more effective your thinking will become. Since most of our beliefs are held in our subconscious minds, introspection is required to uncover what we really believe.

Willpower Versus Imagination

When willpower and imagination come into conflict, the power of imagination will always win out. This is so because the will comes from the periphery of the mind and imagination reaches into its core. What does this mean? We use our willpower to try to force behaviors on ourselves that we believe are outside of ourselves. Willpower takes energy that needs to be forced emotionally and thereby increases stress. The use of our willpower operates from a position of constraining energy. Just the word makes one picture a clenched fist raised in the air.

Imagination can be trained and expanded more readily than willpower. Imagination is free flowing and diminishes stress. **The power of our imagination is unlimited because we can conceive of things beyond what we think are our abilities to create.** Imaginative thoughts are energy already in circulation. It is simply up to us first be in attunement so that we can access them in our minds.

Energy Movement in the Spirit-Mind-Body

One of the most important discoveries medicine has made about our bodies is that we are chemical factories. *Certain cells in the brain make various chemicals that affect our mood and how we think.* Depression, agitation, tranquility, fear, anxiety—these and many more emotions are decisively linked to the actions of certain chemicals called neuropeptides and neurotransmitters. Our energy level is at its lowest when we are in a state of depression.

Candace B. Pert, former Chief of Brain Chemistry of the clinical neuroscience branch at the National Institute of Mental Health, was the co-discoverer of the endorphins. Her findings have revolutionized our beliefs about the origins of our feelings. She discovered that every receptor site that she had been looking for within the brain is also found on monocytes, a type of white blood cell that has a pivotal role in the immune response. White blood cells make chemicals that are practically identical to certain peptides that the nervous system produces. During stress, norepinephrine is released. Even mild stress results in killer-cell activity. Additionally, she found that certain chemicals that affect emotion also control the routing and migration of monocytes. Pert's research team found that the cells of the immune system not only have receptors for various neuropeptide chemicals that control mood in the brain, they also make these substances. Neuropeptides are natural chemicals known to affect such basic functions as sleep, tension, appetite, drug and tobacco use. The entire lining of the intestinal tract, from the esophagus through the large intestine, is lined with cells containing neuropeptides and receptors for them. This explains why we get upset stomachs in response to outward events.

No major sector of the immune system is without a hard wire connection to the brain. **Many of the nervous system's synapses are situated near the thymus and spleen.** Also note here that the thymus is located near the heart. The heart is our connection to our soul. It follows that when we are not *acting from the heart* or *our hearts are broken* it is much easier for us to become ill. The thymus transforms T-cells into functional cells. They patrol for potentially dangerous microbes. B-cells manufacture antibodies that are specifically directed against foreign antigen. At times, there may be a concentration of mast cells, the immune cells become packed with lumps or grains of concentrated chemicals.

Molecules in the Body

Every second a massive information exchange is occurring in your body. In the beginning of this book you read that we are vibrational beings. You learned that each organ of the body has its own specific beat. They have different vibration frequencies. Chinese doctors listen to several pulses because each of our messenger systems possesses a specific humming tune. Our emotions are expressed through electrical and chemical energy. It is all vibrational energy that is sent out from the physical body through the aura.

Vibrations in our bodies are constantly rising and falling, moving higher and lower, and binding and unbinding. When we enjoy nature, we become in tune with its natural rhythm. More and more healing is done using vibrational sound. It is all vibration of energy. Our emotions can be seen in our faces and bodies. They are visible in the light we send out.

A molecule is the tiniest possible piece of substance that can still be identified as that substance. Each and every molecule of any given substance is composed of the smallest unit of matter—atoms such as carbon and hydrogen and nitrogen—that are bonded together in a configuration specific to that substance.

Invisible forces attract one molecule to another, so that the molecules cohere into an identifiable substance. These invisible forces of attraction can be overcome if enough energy is applied to the substance. (Example: Water changing to steam or ice)
Most of us are familiar with what is considered our first nervous system—the one that works as a result of electrical communication. The preceding section

discussed the brain and explained axons and dendrites. We have a second system called the ligand-receptor system. All we need to know about a ligand is that it binds to cell receptors and forces molecules to change their shapes until chemical energy carrying information enters the cell. Remember energy is always in flux, and it carries information. The second thing to remember is what you learned about the body's energy metaboliz-ers—the endocrine glands (hypothalamus, pineal, pituitary, thymus, adrenals, pancreas, and gonads) communicate with our body's other systems, the neurological, the immune system, and the gastrointesti-nal. The way these glands and systems communicate with each other is through what we call *information molecules*.

We have to look in a microscope to see a cell, but a single cell has all kinds of different receptors ranging from 10,000 to 100,000 of each kind sitting on top of it. People tell us not to be so sensitive, but we can have millions of receptors on top of one nerve cell! No wonder it took researchers until the 70's to find these things. Receptors vibrate in the membrane of cells until the chemicals are bound.

If you have a negative emotional reaction, you will send out negative chemicals. You already knew that. Our cells have receptors for all different kind of emotional messages. You hold the key to the kind of messages you want to send. After your receptors receive your positive or negative message, **it goes inside the cell's interior where the message can change the state of the cell.** This explains how sponta-neous remission or healings over a period of time occur. Our minds and emotions can powerfully direct our cells to determine everything that is happening to them. This is not a haphazard process. Just the right *key* has to be there to enter our receptors. Our cells make new proteins, divide, open or close negative and positive energy, and add or subtract other chemicals. You make all changes on the cellular level. This is how we can choose to make one hand hot and one hand cold. Rabbits in laboratories have been trained to vary the temperature of their ears from hot to cold. Like humans, animals are taught to change the rate of their heartbeat. This is how we make changes in our behaviors, our moods, and of course physically.

You don't want a dull life! The experiences we have in life increase the growth and branching of nerve fibers by neuropeptides. The same chemicals that regulate emotions and branching of brain cells are related to experience and memory. If you hold on to your bad experiences and memories, you produce negative chemicals. New negative thoughts create branches in your brain cells.

You've read about the production of chemicals by the hypothalamus, pineal, and pituitary glands in your brain. However, many cells in the blood make chemicals and pain-killing endorphins that in some instances are identical to those made by brain cells. Blood cells also contain receptor sites for various hormones and chemicals identical to those in the brain.

You have an *anatomic* brain that is part of your mind. Inside the body are brain-like tissues and chemicals that serve brain-like functions. For instance, the blood carries these chemicals. We think the thought *fear* and our faces become white and our blood gathers its forces to flee. When we are having the feeling of embarrassment, our face becomes immediately flush with redness (blood). We feel stress in our lives and this causes our blood pressure to rise. Again our faces become red.

When we adhere to locality in time, always looking ahead or behind, never dwelling in the moment—we create a variety of physical illnesses that Jeremy Rifkin calls "time sickness"—coronary artery disease, hypertension, peptic ulcer disease, irritable bowel syndrome, and the vascular headache syndromes including migraine. In general, any illness in which anxiety and excessive time awareness have been shown to play a role, belong in this growing category of human maladies.

Take a test for yourself. Lean back in a reclining chair, relax, close your eyes, and tell someone, who is observing a watch, how long a minute is. You will most likely underestimate how long it takes. Retraining the time sense of biofeedback, self-reflection, or other forms of deep relaxation increases the awareness of non-local happenings in one's life. Paranormal or extrasensory events regularly become more frequent; precognitive dreams may occur, intuition and creativity may flower.

In summary, you've learned that your emotions increase the strength of the program by increasing the amount of electrochemical activity in the brain. So now we've learned how to change our beliefs from "I'm weak" to "I'm powerful." What's going to happen in the next project you start to work on? It's going to be a little easier, of course. You've got success behind you.

Important Chemical Hormones

Cortisone- Anti-inflammatory chemicals that raise the blood sugar present in the body and modulate the body's Immunological defenses.

Neurotransmitters—acetylcholine, histamine, glycine, dopamine, norepinephrine, serotinin, and GABA. They carry information across the gap, or synapse, between one neuron and the next.

Peptides— They are made up of strings of amino acids. If the cell is the engine that drives all life, then the receptors are the button on the control panel of that engine, and a specific peptide is the finger that pushes that button and gets things started.

Neuropeptides— This natural chemical is known to effect such basic functions as sleep, tension, appetite, drug and tobacco addiction, learning, sex, and pleasure. Peptides are produced by the endocrine and nervous system and are found in endorphins.

Serotonin— Low levels of serotonin produce lack of sleep and concentration, confusion, isolation and sense of being unloved or unworthy of love. Anxiety, insomnia, impaired judgment, blackout, nightmares and sexual dysfunction may be caused by low level of serotonin.

Misalignment of Spirit-Mind-Body Zaps Energy

What is going on in your mind is reflected in your face and body. We judge a person in the first few minutes of seeing them. Our mothers might have told us not to "judge a book by its cover," but in this case, what we see when we look into the eyes and faces of a person, is a very accurate reading of who they are and what they are thinking.

Many of our tensions are created during childhood. If we had unreasonable threats, punishments and demands placed upon us as children, we created tensions to block fears and pain and to deaden the impulses that led to these feelings. **Under tension, sensitivity is diminished.** A person with emotional blocks creates chronic muscle tension that interrupts flow. If the sadness is deep and long-standing, and the blocking continues, the tension will become habit and the capacity to express, frozen. With the growth of habit, awareness dims. You can have several blocks.

The blockages create a pattern of muscle tensions that affect movement, posture, growth, and therefore structure. Even changes in the skin tone and temperature may occur. The feet and legs of people affected by diabetes have a blue tone due to lack of circulation. People who refuse to feel their emotions create diabetes and later they are unable to feel in their bodies. Blocks impede the normal flow of energy in the body. They impede not just the chemical or mechanical energy, but that special life force which gives the others meaning. **Beliefs, perceptions, and needs are the true energizers of human action. Blocks disrupt the constant flow of feeling and purpose.**

Holding on to anger, revenge, and guilt causes our muscles to tighten and restricts the flow of movement and energy. When a person's walk is heavy, it reflects an attitude of holding on to negativity. Guilt feelings keep us down. A better choice is seeking self-correction. The book *Psycho-cybernetics* suggests to us that we are occasionally off course, but we have the ability to right ourselves at any moment. The more we choose to learn about ourselves, the more we will learn and *right* ourselves. The question is, "What have I been choosing to teach myself wrongly?" Most of the time, we find that denial of a problem causes effects worse than the problem. When we are happy, peaceful, and harmonious with everything in and around us, our step becomes lighter and we experience the fullness of life.

Fear makes our shoulders contract. It robs us of our connection with our deeper selves. When our shoulders are contracted we are affecting both our lungs, through which we breathe life, and our hearts through which we pump our blood, the other carrier of life. When we flee from central fears, such as death, pain, and isolation, then we are giving them our energy. To run from death, we deaden ourselves. When we cut off fear, we are also cutting off all our feelings. We create a pseudo self, with pseudo feelings. To avoid being left out, we become something we are not, and so leave ourselves out. We find giving up on being wrong is so hard. Wrongness is just a temporary identity crisis you have to give up if you want to live on a higher level.

You have never seen an Olympic winner with poor posture. When we are out of alignment with our purpose, we make ourselves out of alignment physically. When we don't use our muscles correctly to hold up our skeleton, we deplete our energy. We hold our heads forward and distort the correct alignment of our spine and head when we rely on the logical, rational thinking of our brain all of the time, rather than doing creative thinking. Creative thinking is the source of our inventions, the arts, cures and discoveries.

All thinking creates energy and movement that results in change. When we do not have faith in life or confidence in ourselves or that our Creator has already given us what we need, we become physically mis-aligned. We hunch our shoulders forward and round our backs as if we are carrying a great weight. The person who feels overburdened is physically bent, broad, rounded, and has hunched shoulders. His head is dropped onto his chest, his pelvis and thighs are immobilized, and his knees are rigidly locked with the legs and feet tightly contracted. As a result, we constrict the air intake of our lungs. We can not live without breath, and when we take only short breaths, we have no exuberance for life.

Sloped shoulders often reflect our life-long reluctance to take on the responsibility of our lives. Others will retract their shoulders as if pulling back from life. This causes misalignment of the spinal cord and causes the spine to sway inward at the lower back. When there is no sense of purpose, everything in a person's life, including his spine, lacks direction, strength, and balance. When the spine is out of alignment, the body is easily toppled over. To know if you are in alignment, look and see if there is a straight line from your ear lobe to the middle of your shoulder to the middle of your hip, to middle of your knee and finally to the middle of your anklebone. In the same way, our lives become unbalanced when we are out of alignment.

When we slouch forward, it makes every action more difficult, and it makes life seem burdensome. When we are spiritually out of balance, our every move is weighted down by gravity. Our nervous system constantly endeavors to come to terms with messages from our muscles informing us that we are being pushed down or weighted down. People who feel overburdened are bent forward. People who bend backward are resisting and pushing against gravity. A backward bowing person reflects rigid and fixed ideas about right and wrong. They are often pushing toward what they think they want. They contain their feelings, especially those of tenderness and those of hurt.

The next section will discuss the effect of locked muscles. We can actually lose sensitivity in the legs and feet. These people don't know how to let go of things. They stay in unbearable work or love relationships. They feel stuck and chronically in pain. There is almost no end to the pain they are willing to endure. A definite sign of energy depletion is that their movements are rigid, broken, and without flow. The head is usually tilted to one side and the eyes are vacant and distant. The person is unable to withstand pressures from within and without. A person who feels good about himself moves his pelvis with free and easy movement. A person who feels a lack of self worth has a rigid pelvis movement.

The very way that we hold our heads tells us of our relationship with everything. Alignment of the head with the backbone and shoulders keeps us from fatigue, keeps our eyes focused forward, and keeps us facing in the right direction.

What does holding your head too far forward say? These people have trouble with relationships. They do all their thinking with the brain rather than emotionally or intuitively. On the other hand, a head tilted back causes tension at the base of the skull and tension in the jaw with a tightly drawn scalp. This person is holding back his energy which causes a lack of luster in his eyes. A person with a tilted head can not approach anyone or anything directly. A person who feels happy, on purpose, confident, or in love will walk with their head and body in straighter alignment. Such a person also walks lighter.

The very act of raising your chin causes you to feel more energized, more positive, be more alert, and stand more erect. Changing your physiology causes changes your attitude in the same way that changing your thinking changes your physiology and attitude. Whenever a person feels good about himself, he invariably walks with his chin held high. When a person feels depressed, his chin drops down.

The movement of the head and body is honest. It tells us what is going on in our mind. A friend named Beverly was unhappy in her job because she felt that her supervisors treated her as an inferior. Each time Beverly talked about her problems at work, she hung her chin on her chest like a small child. Obviously, her body was reflecting her view.

The top half of our bodies may be too heavy for our legs if we have spent a lifetime puffing ourselves up to appear grander than we are. We often describe such a person as not having a leg to stand on. A top-heavy body has collected a large amount of stagnant energy. Other people have under-developed top halves because they have refused to act in a mature way. The top half of the body actually looks childlike because they have stopped the circulating flow of energy from top to bottom. They have stayed too earth bound and not sought spiritual fulfillment in their lives.

Individuals showing extreme displacement are unable to contact major areas of feeling and vitality. They move and live deeply divided, experiencing constriction as an unremitting constraint. Men are more often displaced upward, women downward. Women who are heavier at the bottom are described as pear-shaped. A person with a larger top, the military general type, has a hunger for importance,. A contracted, rigid lower half blocks the flow of energy downward, leaving the individual ungrounded and unable at times to contain impulses. Those with a tight, small, under-charged upper portion do not allow for aggressive action. Unable to reach or strike out, they have the tendency is toward passivity. They are incapable of taking any action at all.

The knees are indicators of our energy. We've all had a doctor check our response by hitting the front of our knees. Some doctors check out the back of the knees because this is a key pressure point site. Forcing a man to his knees has always been experienced as humiliating or submitting to control. Ever wonder why our knees shake when we are frightened? In Chinese medicine, the knees are felt to be related to the kidneys, our filtering system. The kidneys in turn are related to both the water element and the sexual organs. Water in this system relates to fear.

A lady named Elise told of experiencing such fear while giving a speech that her knees literally became locked more and more tightly as her speech progressed. By the end of the speech, she was unable to bend her knees and had to walk to her seat as if she had two casts on her legs. She was actually surprised that they were able to bend enough for her to sit down.

The most revealing reflection of our "core being" or "essence" is the eye. You can tell the status of a person's health, their level of honesty, and their mental and emotional states by looking at the eyes. Ever wonder why one eye is larger than the other? The left eye, referred to as the receptive eye (Yin or female), reflects the relationship you had with your mother. If your mother gave you a sense of self worth, security and nourishment, then your left eye reflects it. If you didn't have a good relationship with your mother, your left eye will be smaller because anxiety and fear of abandonment have stained all your experiences.

What does the right eye reveal? It is the eye of personality. It is the opposite of the left eye because it reflects the "extrinsic" or "doing" layer. It reflects relationship with our father (Yang, masculine, outgoing eye). If your father showed you the ways of the world, then you are better able to deal with your relationships. If your father wasn't around or if he failed to teach you about relationships, then you developed a sense of distrust in people. We've met the person with the control issue, who felt the need to compensate, and attempted to take over and run the show. A person with a good sense of self-worth does not have difficulty receiving energy from others. This kind of person tells others how to be and is able to look outside himself.

Even if we have impaired sight, or our perceptions have been distorted by our upbringing, all of us have what is called "the eye of wisdom" or "the seat of mind consciousness," which is called the third eye. It is a part of your mind and is located in your head behind the eyebrows. Remember that you learned that the pineal gland is the body's **"light meter,"** our connection to the earth's electromagnetic field. It is the body's regulator of regulates because it regulates everything that is happening in the body. The supratrochlear nerve runs between the eyes, and we know that nerves are activated by electrical impulses. This nerve's location at the third eye is the reason we can "see" and "imagine" things that are not in the physical. A psychic hired by the police to solve a murder will see the death scene with the third eye.

A person with persistent contraction of his eyebrows and the muscles around his eyes narrows his vision or focuses attention upon a limited field. You create wrinkles in your forehead when this area is knotted together with ridges of tension and you are feeling a sense of intensity and/or bound anger. Wrinkles reveal our attitude toward life. When we see vertical wrinkles between the eyes, this suggests a person who is overly concerned about his/her family. They do not see the broad picture and focus too narrowly on things.

Even a person's skin reflects their life style and nature. For instance, broken capillaries reveal a drinker or high blood pressure, redness of skin suggests high blood pressure while splotchy skin suggests water retention.

The handshake is the first opportunity to make physical contact with a person. We can know so much about a person through this form of touch because it tells about their energy. How they shake hands tells us whether they have a sense of power or weakness. In fact, most people initially measure the character, integrity, and personal strength of another person by their handshake. A firm handshake, accompanied by a full look in the eyes and a smile, tells the other person that they have met a real human being who is there with an important message.

It is a good idea to become aware of the message you are sending with your handshake. **It tells of your energy and attitude toward life.** Practice with someone you trust will be honest about your handshake. It is important to have a full, firm handshake. You might even take your second finger and extend it a little further up the arm to increase your contact with the person. The slightest movement with the hand indicates whether you can be trusted or not. A deceitful person will move his hand slightly to the right initially, which indicates that this person will not be committed to his word.

On the other hand, sometimes women take the "halfway approach" to handshaking by sticking out the ends of their fingers, almost as if they expect the other person to kiss the back of their hand. This is also called the model's handshake. It tells the other person that this woman has an overly "royal" opinion of herself.

When a person does the "lawyer's handshake," they are holding their palms parallel to the floor with the fingers spread apart. It's like "give me the money." The preacher's handshake almost pulls you forward. In fact, that person might put his other hand on your arm to pull you in. This person wants you to like and trust him.

You can use the power of touch to greatly increase your influence. By touching someone appropriately, you will appear more likable and trustworthy Your body is divided into roughly three zones with regard to touch. The first is the "public zone," the area from your elbows to your fingertips. The second is the "social" zone—your arms, shoulders, and back, which your family and friends touch or pat in passing. The third is the private or intimate zone. You can touch a person in the public zone without offending. When you touch a person for emphasis, either on the hand or the lower part of the arm, he will perceive you to be a warmer, friendlier, more sincere and believable person. You can gently touch a person on the elbow with your hand and feel a closer connection.

How the Mind Works

In the last few decades Science has begun to explore and develop a better understanding of the ways in which the mind and body affect each other. In order to better understand the total mind/body unity and experience it more fully, we need to look for the specific bridges that strongly connect mind and body. Every bridge that we discover will give us another avenue of mind-body communication, and will therefore suggest to us appropriate techniques for making use of that communication.

The first concept we must understand is that the mind is more than just our conscious mind; it includes our sub-conscious or unconscious mind. Our conscious mind arises from the much vaster sub-conscious, and we remain unaware of most of our own mental processes and patterns. Our conscious mind is like the beam of a small flashlight cast about within a dark cavernous room. We experience eruptions of the sub-conscious into conscious awareness in the form of dreams, sudden inspirations, intuitions but usually we are not aware of the obsessions, compulsions, drives, and neuroses that reside in the sub-conscious mind and influence us without our knowledge.

The purpose of the conscious mind is to protect the survival of the person. It stands on the cusp of the present and the future. It is not a master but a servant of the person. It serves desire and animal instinct that comes from the sub-conscious.

The conscious mind gives us the ability to program ourselves because it tells the nervous system what to accept or reject. It retrieves information from the memory and it links us to the past. It uses this information in all its activities. The conscious mind also retrieves material from the sub-conscious in the form of imagination that enables it to carry out its function. It focuses on detail and discriminates the finer facts of one pattern from another. It gives us the ability to select material that goes into our sub-conscious mind.

The main two aspects of the conscious mind are its broad awareness of the surrounding environment and its aspect of focused attention. Focused attention is moveable at will.

The conscious mind does our decision-making, problem solving, calculating, reasoning, planning, warning system (awareness of what is going on around us), and it controls our motor skills. We can improve the uses of the conscious mind through practice. Neural pathways become stronger and more numerous with repetition. Parts of the conscious mind atrophy if not utilized.

We will not go deeply into this subject here, since the existence of the sub-conscious is a well-established scientific fact and field of study. Right now the thing we need to know is that the sub-conscious includes all the brain-functions that we are not aware of, including those that regulate the autonomic nervous system. The sub-conscious mind also operates the heart, controls the blood vessels and glands, and that keeps watch over all the other bodily processes that are not under voluntary control. It is therefore through the sub-conscious that we will find most of our bridges between the conscious mind and the body. The subconscious mind is less focused than the conscious mind, but it is better at perceiving subtle or broader patterns that the conscious. It helps you retrieve specific information. Also, it creates or changes learned behaviors through self-hypnosis, autosuggestion, or hypnosis.

Our conscious attention only casts a pencil-flashlight beam on the content of our minds. The sub-conscious is much vaster. It contains the light and the dark, including the id and the animal instincts. Most of our mental power is locked up here. **It is the source of our mental energy**—it is a jungle and a jumble (an idiot child). It contains a multitude of contradictions and is the repository of emotional experience. It is the source of our desires, manifest in our dreams, imagination, etc.

Every automatic habit and personal idiosyncrasy originates in the brain. The conscious mind can not run without the subconscious. Through suggestion, we can use it to affect our automatic processes such as heartbeat and breathing. We can even change aspects of the conscious mind and emotions. The suggestions can be hypnotic. Different kinds of suggestions are autosuggestions, affirmations, mental imagery, sound, verbal, prayer, and meditation. They can alter harmful patterns in the subconscious and encourage all beneficial patterns. Also, they can expand awareness into this hidden vast inner region. Actions and habit responses will reflect negative conditioning until the nervous relay syndrome is deliberately changed on a subconscious level.

Your subconscious mind is where you hold the expectations based on your belief and heritage. The beliefs about energy expenditure are held in your subconscious. Your beliefs determine how much energy you choose in different areas of beliefs. The subconscious contains all of our memories—the organized (long-term) memories and our unorganized memories (memories that we may never retrieve.)

Self-observation gives us the power of self-change and selecting our own goals. It allows us the ability to look within without fearing what we will see. We are not the person that we have created. If we listen to our inner self, we can always make the right choices because the inner self has no interest in and is not governed by our past events. Nor does the inner self have any interest or need to control our future. Changing ourselves begins with observing ourselves. The inner self is intelligent because it only knows what is going on in the present moment.

We have various ways of describing the way our mind is working. We might say that we are in a state of mindfulness, meaning that we are consciously aware of what is going on around us, that we are not only attuned to the impute of our sensory perceptions, but we are utilizing the information in our thoughts. Mindlessness, of course, would be just the opposite. Everyone knows to some degree how their mind is working, whether they are absent minded, out of their minds, or mindful. When we ask most people where their mind is, they will point to the location of their brain. Earlier in this book it was discussed how the billions of cells in the brain receive sensory information that is analyzed by the brain's cerebral cortex and then relayed to other cells in the body. Some people will point to their bodies to indicate the location of their mind. To them the mind is enlivened energy that is transmitted from cell to cell throughout the body. Not only is this true, but this enlivened energy activates the body to produce chemicals and electrical energy in our bodies.

The Mind is Local and Non-local.

"What you see with your eyes shut is what counts."—Lame Deer Sioux Medicine Man

What is the process of creation, or how does the mind work? The sequence of the mind is from pure energy, through a mental pattern, and then into observable manifestation.

If I were to ask you to picture or imagine a lemon, you would shift your thinking to the space just between and above your eyebrows called the Third Eye. When you use your Third Eye to imagine a candle burning in front of a ring of fire around you, your mind is outside your body. The belief that our minds are contained within our bodies is a limiting idea.

We have all received a phone call from a long time friend who said that they had been thinking about us for a long time. And we realized that we had also been thinking about them. Many of us receive phone calls and we already know who the caller is before we pick up the phone. The thoughts, mind energy, are actually transmitted from one body, through time and space, to the other person. The mind is nonlocal in space and time, so our interaction with each other is a foregone conclusion. Nonlocal minds are merging minds since they are not "things" that can be walled off and confined to moments in time or point-positions in space. Helen Keller said that with her mind she was transported to Italy and actually felt she was there with her sense perceptions while her physical body remained in the U.S.

We can go one step further and describe negative energy as mind energy sent outside from one body to the other body. Most of us have had the experience of entering a room where two people had been arguing and felt the remains of negative energy.

Because the nonlocal mind is a reality, the world becomes a place of interaction and connection, not one of isolation and disjunction. How might our ethical and moral behavior change if everyone believed in the nonlocal mind? We would realize that what we think and do affects the collective consciousness thinking.

Memory

The mind contains mental patterns and mental processes that we are not aware of. They tend to repeat and extend themselves. They make up their own rules. We can not rely on our **patterned thinking** because most of it is based on false or outdated information. Ask most people for their advice, and they will base it their own experiences or patterned thinking. How many people can you list who always have original ideas who monitor all their thoughts?

The mental patterns of the mind are held in the mind's memory. Our memory resides in each of the cells of our body. The cells of the immune system remember to attack outside microorganisms. The memory in the cells of our muscles holds on to unreleased emotions and feelings that cause them to tighten and stay in a state of retraction.

The memory holds on to your belief system held in your sub-conscious and it determines whether you will be successful or unsuccessful in the following areas: habitual perceptions, physical health (weight, harmful habits such as smoking and drinking) and life styles, in the areas of finances, emotional stability, and productivity, your level of spirituality, and relationships. The most important memory we have is our spiritual memory. This is where the truth is held about our value and worth. If you see life as a struggle with forces opposing you, it is because you are not in touch with your spiritual memory.

Autosuggestion

We use autosuggestion, also called self-talk, to send messages to the subconscious mind which in turn helps us to lose weight, quit smoking, and make other kinds of changes. We say over and over what we want to become. Autosuggestion creates a new kind of reality when it is combined with imagination, a reality that is different and better than before, free of past echoes. It always considers doing things easily. The conditioned reflex that produced the harmful behavior is removed once a more appropriate idea is accepted by the subconscious. When you know how to direct positive thoughts, they work as a loving kind of brain washing. You can do it verbally or through silent thoughts ("self-suggestions") influencing yourself to change in a determined direction. Positive conditioning works the same way that negative conditioning does, except in reverse. **Awareness clears space in the mind for a new set of habits**. It helps us do some mental house-cleaning in our minds. The ability to calm the physical body enables us to calm the mind and to be more aware, creative, and receptive of intuitive information.

We can use auto-suggestion, self-suggestion, as a technique that teaches body relaxation by means of a form of self-hypnosis. Intelligent and critically minded subjects can induce autosuggestive states. Developed about eighty years ago by German psychiatrist Johannes Schultz, the method directs participants to focus their concentration on specific parts of their bodies with verbal messages such as "my heartbeat is calm and regular." These messages are repeated over and over as in a chant, and then the attention is focused on a different part of the body, where the process is repeated.

Autogenic Training helped stimulate the development of biofeedback training as well as some behavioral and imagery-based therapies. The core of Autogenic Training has six physiologically oriented steps: heaviness and warmth in the extremities, regulation of cardiac activity and respiration, abdominal warmth and cooling of the forehead.

The training can help alleviate bronchial asthma and tuberculosis; disorders of the gastrointestinal tract; "cardiac neuroses" and functional problems of the heart, angina pectoris, high blood pressure, and other circulatory afflictions; disorders of the endocrine system, the urogential system and pregnancy, diseases of the eyes and skin; epilepsy; stuttering; alcoholism; and problems with sleep.

The Methods of Autogenic Training and Progressive Relaxation

* sensory and kinesthetic awareness-(awareness of information receive through the five senses)
* control of autonomic processes-(such as heartbeat, breathing, and digestion)
* efficient modulation of sensory input-(making the correct responses)
* sensorimotor coordination-(we achieve the three preceding bulleted items and movement with ease and grace. A relaxed body is the most efficient utilizer of energy.
* the articulation and coordination of particular muscle groups
* grace and efficiency of posture, carriage, and movement
* new patterns of movement
* flexibility of facial and gestural expression
* general relaxation as well as the relaxation of particular body parts during complex behaviors
* recuperation from stress
* vitality
* awareness and control of emotions and mental processes
* sensory, kinesthetic, emotional and intellectual pleasure

Superconscious mind

How would you like to have greater insights, to know the decision you are making is perfect, to know that you have the right answers? That would save a lot of time and energy! Want to really shine? We call it an illumination when we receive information from the universal level of mind. In order to do this you have to first get rid of your energy blockages and you have to shut down the activity of the conscious mind and the sub-conscious mind. This involves the work of undoing all negative processes and patterns so that the subconscious can then gain access to the superconsciousness. Your subconscious mind has been acting like a sponge all your life taking in all kinds in information. This is why people have to spend time alone to learn what they want to know. You don't have to go anywhere, you just need to open up your subconscious mind.

When you feel something or have a thought, chemical messengers come from the brain, the stomach, and other chemical production places in the body and express what that feeling was. Whenever you have a simultaneous feeling, emotion, or intention, you have the materialization of these chemicals throughout the body. There are sixty different neuropeptides, each associated with different states of mind and emotions. Every single cell in the body manufactures these at the same instant of time as you have a feeling.

The chemical energy transmission system is based on receptors, which, of course, receive, and effectors that send along the information *after* it has passed through our brain, the main network of the conscious mind. We are receiving all the same information, but our individual programming enables us or prevents us from acting upon the information.

If you have read the biographies of successful people, you know that they credit their success to something greater than they are. Mozart would wake up and write out whole symphonies without changing a note. Most great inventors said that an idea came to them from outside themselves. Most of us have experienced ideas so profound we knew we didn't learn them, they just came to us. We call this provider the super-conscious mind and it is reached through the subconscious. The superconscious mind is the Mind of Being. The superconscious mind has total awareness, pure being, perfect intelligence, wisdom, knowledge, and love. We want to stay open to access super-intelligence.

The first principle of this book, The Principle of Energy, discussed how everything in the universe is based upon one energy. We learned that energy carries information and is intelligent. When we tap into this intelligent energy, we are able to be more creative in our thinking, writing, creating—everything we do. It transcends the individual and is available for all.

Consciousness at the highest level is achieved at this state. If you don't feel you are there yet, saying aloud the following sentences will help you achieve consciousness:

I may open up consciousness with a panoramic view over both inner and outer worlds. Attentive and present, I am conscious of everything without filters of preferences.

I can, instead, focus on a single object, to the exclusion of everything else, taking consciousness to a level of maximum intensity.

Through introspection, I can retrace consciousness to its source and let it merge back into itself. In this way I become conscious of my Self as empty of all content, unconfined by space or time.

The Breath as an Energy Source

Our breath intake reflects the amount of energy we will have to fuel our lives. The breath is such an important factor because it is the one major function under dual control by the voluntary and the autonomic nervous systems. We are able to consciously control our breathing, but when we drop our conscious control, breathing proceeds automatically. We can deliberately speed up and slow down our breathing, or take large breathes or small ones; but most of the time we are not even aware of our breathing and its pace is regulated for us, adjusting to the body's needs. Under stress, our breath will automatically speed up, and when we are calm and relaxed, it will automatically slow down. We can even hold our breath for a long time, but before we can harm ourselves, automatic response will take over and force us to breathe whether we want to or not.

So, the breath is a bridge between the conscious mind and unconscious bodily processes. How can we make use of this bridge? We know that when we feel peaceful and calm, our breathing is slow, easy, and relaxed. If we understand that the mind and body are one, we will realize that this is not a case of the mind being the cause, and the body showing the effect, or the body being the cause, and the mind showing the effect. The two things work together. Is it peacefulness making us breathe easily, or is it easy breathing making us peaceful? The answer is, both.

If calmness makes us breathe easily, then breathing easily can make us calm. If we are upset or agitated, we can help restore ourselves to calm and alter our mood simply by controlling our breath and breathing *as if we were* calm. Focusing our attention on the breath also brings our mind away from distressing thoughts that fuel our anxiety, and so allows the anxiety to die down.

Breathing exercise

To breathe naturally, we must sit in an upright posture, not slump down. Slumping puts pressure on the diaphragm and tends to close off the lower lungs. Many people only breathe into the top part of the lungs, and you can see their chests puff out as they inhale. To fully breathe we must breathe all the way into the bottom of the lungs, taking air all the way down. Only in this way do we get enough oxygen and keep our lower lungs clear! Most of the lung's capacity is in the lower lung. You should breathe from the diaphragm. If you are breathing properly, your belly will rise and fall like the belly of a dog, but your chest should hardly move at all.

Always breathe through the nose, not the mouth. The nose helps filter the air and keep out impurities.
Try it: sit erect, but relaxed, not rigid. Your spine and neck should be aligned. Take a big cleansing breath into the bottom of the lungs and exhale. Now just allow yourself to breathe easily, letting air flow in to the bottom of the lungs, and when it feels right, easily exhale. Continue this natural, easy breathing, never forcing either the inhale or the exhale, but just allowing the breath to rise and fall by itself. Keep your attention on the breathing. Feel your stomach gently rise and fall as you breathe. Feel the coolness and smooth texture of

the air coming in and feel the warmth of the air going out.

Doesn't this kind of breathing make you feel calm and relaxed? Practice this breathing consciously. Whenever you find yourself breathing erratically or in short, shallow, rapid breaths, restore this calm, deep breathing. If you find yourself breathing through your mouth, close it and breathe through your nose. Soon you will breathe in this calming, healthy way naturally and automatically. Simply breathing in this way will bring more harmony and peace into your life, reduce stress, and assist the body in healing and in warding off ailments.

The Power of Our Words

We already know the power and energy of our words. They can instruct, inspire and enlist us to take action. At times we do not realize that we have already formed an opinion or felt so strongly for a cause until we express our ideas into words. Choose your words carefully. The words that are chosen create states that can affect the thoughts that are in your brain.

Be specific about how you really feel, and be careful about how you describe your feelings. These feelings and emotions are only indications; they are not you. Don't downplay your words. Choose them as carefully as your thoughts. Your mind inputs the information you send it. What if you started sending words like *brilliant, incredible, enthralling, compelling, spectacular, extraordinary, unstoppable, beautiful,* or *fabulous*?

For example, we often say that we are depressed, a serious and unhappy emotion. This is a strong word that conveys a strong emotional intensity.

To describe yourself as depressed is a strong indication that needs to be accurately diagnosed so that you can make changes in your physiology, your surrounding or your state. Perhaps you need to describe your feelings more accurately. Are you really lonely, tired, or worried?

Words are the vehicles we use to play games with others and ourselves. They do not have power over you. They are useful to express the emotions that ignite us to action so we must be attuned, discerning and accurate about our interpretations.

What we say to ourselves becomes real in our bodies and our world. Want to know what you have been saying to yourself? Look at the happiness or unhappiness of your relationships. Our relationships with others only mirror the one we have with our self. When we recognize and then stop critical, depreciating self-talk, we stop one of the sources of our low self-esteem and destructive habit patterns. An unhappy relationship with ourselves, coupled with all the other kinds of unhappy relationships, depletes our energy the most. People who hold on to anger or loss after the death of a loved one or the death of a marriage, live in energy deficiency for an average of two years and for some a lifetime.

Those who see humans as energy beings know that their loved one's energy is not gone. Those who are divorced eventually realize that they weren't putting enough energy into the marriage, or they were putting in negative energy. The experiences of life are to teach us to call upon our loving, accepting, forgiving and empowering inner voices no matter what has happened. Our attitudes expressed through our mental energy give us the opportunity to enhance our self-esteem, relationships, productivity, creativity, and even make us healthier by strengthening the immune system! There are several books that will help you discover the source of your negative thinking. They teach the use of dialoguing, personalized affirmations, wishing wheels, free-flow writing, energy prints, and toning to shift thoughts, feelings and habit patterns.

We have believed the idea that we cannot control our thoughts, emotions, feelings, and actions. Yet we were created with all the internal resources— our minds, nervous system, and immune system— everything that we need so that we can be in control. To successfully access your mind energy, you must learn how to be calm, balanced and at peace, no matter what situation you are in.

We know that we can affect the body by our conscious intentional actions, as when we throw a ball or ride a bicycle. Such activities also affect conditions in our body that our conscious minds do not directly control, such as our rate of heartbeat, metabolic rate, etc. There is certainly nothing mysterious about the fact that we can engage in certain activities that promote our well being and refrain from others that cause us to feel poorly. We are constantly using our conscious minds to regulate aspects of our physiology in this way. Exercise, diet, posture, rest, and the formation of healthy habits, all of these are ways in which our conscious choices indirectly affect the inner, "involuntary" mechanisms of the body. This is simple common sense.

But there is one more physical activity, one that we would not usually think of, through which we can influence the biochemical universe of the body. It is our most elaborate physical performance: speech. Speech forms another special "bridge" by which the conscious mind can affect bodily processes. The use of words, either spoken or silently thought, to affect "involuntary" bodily processes is called "suggestion." The word "suggestion" connotes a verbal cue, but we will see that suggestion does not have to be verbal. Suggestion takes many forms. However, one powerful form of mental suggestion is that which uses words.

How is it that someone can affect part of the body just by speaking to it? How can I perform such feats as chilling my hand by repeating over and over, "I am chilling my hand?" How could I overcome a depression by telling myself, "my brain is now increasing its levels of serotonin and endorphins?"

To understand the strength of verbal suggestion over bodily processes and mental and emotional states, we must see that speech, which we normally think of as a conscious activity, perhaps the quintessential conscious activity, is anything but. We are conscious of what we are saying, but the simplest acts of speech rests upon deep and intricate subconscious foundations. Think of the hundreds of physical acts and the feats of mental agility that go into the utterance of a single sentence! Yet it comes out so glibly, so quickly! Through conscious attention we could never master such a complex act. We cannot even understand such a simple fact as that we begin many (most!) of our sentences without knowing how they are going to end, and yet bring them to a successful conclusion! We are able to do this because so much of the act of speech has become automatic; most of the act of speaking is carried out subconsciously. The roots of everyday speech are in the subconscious mind. Speech is constantly rising up from the sub-conscious like an undulating sea serpent showing its coils briefly above the waves to consciousness before slipping below. We never see the head or the tail, just the flash of its scaly back. Conscious attention is thereby liberated to concern itself with such matters as conveying the precise meaning we intend. Not only is the "deep structure" of language buried in the subconscious, but so are all our associations with individual words. Every word resonates in the subconscious differently.

We may be certain, then, that the subconscious mind **understands** our language. Our ordinary, native tongue is not alien to the subconscious mind; our everyday language is as natural to the subconscious as it is to the conscious mind, because the **subconscious learned it first.**

If, therefore, the conscious mind wishes to say something to the subconscious mind, it needs to look no further than ordinary language for one means of communication. The subconscious can simply be talked to. Of course, how the sub-conscious will respond can be a little unpredictable; the sub-conscious is, after all, irrational. The subconscious is like an idiot child. It will do what you tell it, but as in controlling a child you must exercise firmness, consistency, and simplicity of command. Patience and repetition also help.

In giving oneself suggestion aimed at the subconscious mind, experience shows these methods useful:

1. *Be confident; take the attitude that you are in charge and your sub-conscious will respond to your suggestion.*

2. *Keep your suggestions few and simple. In the beginning, it is best to work with one single suggestion at a time, and only proceed to a new suggestion when it is clear the first has become operative.*

3. *Begin with tasks that it is comparatively easy for the sub-conscious to bring about. The subconscious*

*easily affects moods, emotions, attitudes, and per-
sonality, for instance. It is best to start with simple
suggestions such as "I am serene" or "I laugh easily" and leave, say, stigmata and glowing in the
dark to a future lifetime!*

4. *Repeat the suggestion regularly. It is best if it is
given at the same time each day; the subconscious
becomes trained to accept suggestions given at the
accustomed time in the accustomed way. Before
sleep or upon awaking are two good times for the
giving of suggestion, because at these times the
doors of the subconscious are ajar. Suggestion in
these cases will need to be prepared beforehand for
deploying at the proper moment.*

5. *Along with the verbal suggestion, imagine the state
which the verbal suggestion represents; i.e., if you
are suggesting serenity, imagine this state and what
it feels like as you give the verbal suggestion, "I
will be serene; I am becoming serene; I am serene."*

6. *Give only positive suggestions. These are for
beneficial outcomes.*

7. *Do not entertain any negative suggestions. If
harmful suggestions enter consciousness, banish
them and replace them with positive suggestions.*

After a little practice, when you have estab-
lished confidence in your own power to stay healthy
and thereby energetic, you will find it easy to give
yourself such suggestions as "I am resistant to infection," "I am filled with health and well-being," "I am
energetic," "my bodily processes all work in harmony,"
"my pain is lessening," "healing forces are converging
on my (such-and-such an organ, injury, etc.)."

The Power of Whole Brain Thinking

We achieve peak experiences in our lives when we think or act out of a deep conviction. How does our mind use our brain to do *whole thinking* and access what is true? How can we feel that not only what we're doing is true and correct and also feel comfortable in operating and taking action on a foundation of deeply held convictions? Where do these convictions lie? How do we *know that we know* with certainty? The answers lie in knowing how the brain functions optimally.

The brain acts a central switchboard. It processes data consistent with what it is used to. When we ask it to process new and very different information, we say the brain first has to *register* it because it doesn't know where to store the information. We have to *create a new file*. And then we have to present the information over and over. We have been taught that we are primarily either a right brain user or a left brain user. Unfortunately, we have not been taught the power of whole brain thinking. That is, using your right side to create, to see the beauty in the world and then using the left side of your brain to put your dreams and pictures into action. The right and left hemispheres interact all of the time though each has their own functions. Do you know that the right side of your brain produces more chemicals than your left side? The right side is more emotional. It is easier to think creatively when your brain is operating with the left and right sides more in synchrony. You can more easily examine and use the information taken in by the left and right sides of the brain, without the interference of extraneous thoughts.

For a right-handed person, the left hemisphere of the brain acts as a sort of "an office manager." It tries to make sense out of the huge quantities of new and stored information; the left side sifts and categorizes information. You speak, add, subtract, measure, organize, compartmentalize, and tell time from the left side. It makes inferences and predictions based on that information. The fact that we can put thoughts in language and give precise reasons for why we do things is largely a direct result of the left side of the brain. The left side overshadows the role of the right side. The left side has been conditioned into thinking that certain things are good for as human beings—when in fact those things may really be detrimental to our growth and well-being.

The right side is a key to the flexibility of our minds. For instance, the right side can identify a shape suggested by only a few lines—visual closure. The right brain serves as a center of many of our intuitive, creative mental functions. This is when we experience a sense of wholeness, unboundedness, infinite correlation, well being, and intense wakefulness. It is when we tend to have much greater awareness of the richness of details, which surround our environment. The right side is where we develop our wonderful sense of awareness of our personal feelings, our sense of connection with everything in the world, and our awareness and connection with others.

Your ability to detect patterns and tendencies in people and things come from your right side. Listen to the right side of your brain, and even when you are given limited pieces of information, you will be able to see the "whole picture" clearly.

We still have what is called the ancient limbic brain, also called the emotional brain. Our brain's right hemisphere is still connected to it. When you are in an alpha state, the state of hypnosis, trying to remember something or in an altered state of consciousness, you are connected to the emotional brain. When you do something because your heart "has spoken" to you, this is where it comes from.

Many people in the business world let the left side of their brain overshadow the role of the right side. They rely on the logic of how things have been, rather than creating how things should be. The left side sees things in their parts rather than seeing the whole. The right brain presents our much-needed conflicts, and when we refuse to "see" them, we make decisions that are not from the heart. The energy charge of our feelings keeps circulating and manifests one way or another.

The people involved in prayer, meditation, chanting, and focused attention are actually increasing the coherence and harmony in their brain wave patterns. They are also increasing the activity of the Corpus Callosum, the mass of nerves connecting the right and left hemispheres of the brain that give them the power of whole brain thinking. Another word for whole brain thinking is called *integrative thinking*, the process of becoming aligned. It is taking the different parts and putting them together so that they form integrity within. The result of integration is a state of flowing. so that there are no sharp edges to the experience or to the being.

The Principle of Connection

The Principle of Connection covers the oneness of spirit-mind-body. The first section discusses the connective tissues that hold the body together. The second section will focus on the how the mind is connected throughout the physical body. The last part will be a discussion on how the spirit is connected to both mind and body and the problems that occur when we think we are three separate parts.

The Connective Tissue of the Body

The connective tissues of our bodies are probably not high up on your reading list. However, to understand how energy flows through your body, you must endure a little anatomy lesson on the description and different forms of the body's connective tissue, where it is located, and how the different varieties function.

Consider your connective tissues as golden threads holding your spirit-mind-body up. Your connective tissue is involved with every cell in your body. Connective tissue is the whitish, gloss sac covering raw bones, the covering of our internal organs, and the lining of our body's cavities.

Connective tissue takes the following forms: tendons, ligaments, cartilage, membranes, and collagen. Protein collagen is thin white fibers that make up sheets and cords.

Seven Facts about Connective Tissue

Connective tissue extends from our heads to our toes and into every part of our bodies.

It is a continuous substance that connects every single part of the body through linings, cables, wrappings and attachments.

It binds specific cells into tissues, tissues into organs, organs into systems.

It bonds muscles to bones with sheaths of fascia.

It not only coats the bones but it connects them to joints.

It surrounds every nerve and every vessel.

It holds all internal structures into place.

We just learned how connective tissue, in its many forms and activities, holds us together from head to toe. The second significant fact is that a transparent fluid called *ground substance* is found in all of the body's connective tissues. You can picture it looking like raw egg white in appearance and consistency. **Ground substance is the liquid through which other fluids, such as hormones, plasma, nutrients, and wastes move.**

Ground substance varies in different locations of the bodies. Every cell and thereby every membrane in the body is directly connected to and affected by *ground substance.* Nutrients, wastes, and gases are moved through *ground substance.* It is important to note here also that hormones, antibodies, and white blood cells are transported by *ground substance.* Hormones, which produce our feelings and emotions, and white blood cells and antibodies, which are responsible for our health, are circulated by the same connective substance.

Interacting with the blood and cellular membranes, *ground substance* acts as a barrier and a helper. When *ground substance* is depleted or the cells of the body experience stress, trauma, malnutrition, fatigue, toxins, and foreign substances the whole body is damaged. Good health, good emotional stability, and good focus and concentration—and all the other good things that happen to us—are the result of the connection and equilibrium of our spirit-mind-body.

Our minds and our bodies are indeed one when we consider that hormone chemicals which produce our happy or sad states also cause our white blood cells and own protective antibodies to function or not to function.

Another connective force in our bodies is long white connective tissue called collagen fibers. The fibers of our organs, the skin, our bones and their attachments, ligaments, tendons, cartilage, and the vessels are collagen. We could say of the collagen network that it is the fiber of our being. Remember this when you read about the fiber of our being in The Connective Spirit.

The collagen network, the connective tissues of our body, knits together the cells of all the organs and limbs, gives them their shape, and arranges them in the proper relationships to one another. Hopefully, you will gain a new appreciation of your collagen fibers.

The whole or oneness our spirits will be discussed in the third section, The Connective Tissue of our Spirits. It is hoped that discussing spirit-mind-body as separate entities is not adding to the illusion of separation. It is simply a means to clarify each topic and then show their connectedness.

We were created so that every part of our bodies is connected. We are connected through the nervous system, the connective tissue, which then connects our internal organs, our muscles and bones. Further connection exists through the *ground substance* fluid that runs through the connective tissue.

The connective tissue in our body is the part of the circulatory system that helps keep all of our parts open and working. In the form of tendons and ligaments it is a tough, flexible meshwork. You know the importance of tendons if you have had knee surgery or had a twisted ligament. In the form of cartilage and bones it is hard. We tend to forget that our bones are very much alive and producing bone morrow. Throughout our lives connective tissue continues to change because it is made up of fluid, fibers, cells, and crystalline parts which can change the concentration of their makeup to do different jobs at different stages. And if we have not exercised our bodies and our minds, the fibers become hard and the fluid does not flow.

The points to remember are: even though our connective tissues take on several forms and act in several different ways, like everything else in our bodies, they are all connected. If our mental attitudes and physical expression have not been in alignment with our spiritual attitudes, our connective tissues work improperly.

Connective Tissue as Liquid Crystal

The ability to behave like a liquid crystal enables connective tissues act as structuring agents. Remember, in the beginning of the book, we were described as crystalline beings because we act as energy transformers? Connective tissues takes on different forms—solid, elastic, wiry, or watery—depending upon its locations and needs. Some times it is solid, others times it is gel. Some places in the body it works with cartilage and bone. Whatever form it takes, it is all connected and another of the means that mind energy travels through the body and the electromagnetic field.

Bones and connective tissues are the major elements of structure in the body. The muscles add motion to this structure. Remember the nerves of the neural system run through the muscles responding to the thoughts that produce mind energy and cause the muscles to act. The bones and ligaments give this network the rigidity necessary for correct posture, while the tendons connect the bones to the muscles so muscular contraction produces specific motions. You need to go back and thank your mother for nagging you to stand up straight because now you realize how proper body posture and alignment enables our body movements to flow with ease and grace, and require less physical energy.

The Connective Tissue of Our Minds

This section answers the question posed in the introduction, *"How can we install surge protectors against outside external negative influences?"* The interpretation of sensory information by our mind lets us choose a positive response (being mindful, in control, relaxed,) or it lets us choose a negative response,' instead allowing us to simply be reactive (mindless, out of control, unrelaxed). The ability to utilize our internal resources is called several things, wholeness, oneness of our being, or oneness of spirit-mind-body. Oneness enables us and endows us with the ability to be in control of our thoughts, our health, our goals, dreams and visions. When we are depressed, in mental or physical pain, and emotionally stressed, our thoughts are also "disjointed," "uncontrolled," and "unclear."

Most importantly, it helps us understand how we are infused in oneness with our Creator. This gives us the power to be a co-creator. This connection enables us to heal our bodies through prayer, meditation, and positive thoughts. It enables us to receive information from the Creator that is outside of what information is stored in our brain. It enables us to know the purpose of our lives and to create through our imagination the vision and then the reality we choose.

Negative states of mind can adversely affect specific organs in specific ways. Sustaining high levels of anxiety for extended periods of time is likely to produce stomach ulcers. Organic damage occurs during sustained states of anger, grief, hatred, and apathy. Instead of acting like a piece of jellied mindless mass, we should realize that we are a finely tuned, precision piece of creation.

Every organ and every cell is affected by the sensations, the feeling states, the attitudes, the opinions, the fantasies, and the voluntary choices of the conscious mind. **All associations made in the cortex create a chemical or electrical reaction and find concrete expression in the body's muscles, the glands, and every cell of the body.**

Some of our learned symptoms are: queasiness, faintness, palpitations, high blood pressure, ulcers, secondary responses to trauma, many skin conditions and allergies, neuropathies of various kinds, imbalances of glandular secretions, including the most powerful hormones of the body, and lapses in the body's immune system. Think of how a simple case of hives creates itching and pain and detracts from using your mind energy. Every time you relive a trauma in your mind, you re-enforce the memory in your body cells. You hands sweat, your stomach becomes upset, your head or back aches. As long as you continue to store the memory and choose to reconnect with it, you will relive the experience.

The Connective Tissue of our Spirits

We have just learned that every cell in our bodies is connected. Also, we learned that our connective tissues, though they are made of different kinds of cells, most of which is collagen, are connected, just as the name implies. Running through all of these connective tissue is, *ground substance,* **an energy carrying substance**, which plays such an important role in our well being. **Now add what we learned about how our minds are in every one of our 100 trillion cells.**

The collective tissue, the nervous system, the circulatory system, the blood system, the immune system, the respiratory system—actually are all connected. So everything that we think affects every cell of our body. We have the power to make ourselves sick or healthy, sad or happy, aware or unaware, and conscious or unconscious. We can behave spiritually or non-spiritually. You get the point. Everything that we are is connected.

The health of our spirit manifests in the health of the mind and the body. For instance, when our will is out of alignment with our Creator's will, we are not fulfilling purpose. Purpose is essential in our lives. Our will or our intention is held in our back, in our spinal cord and nervous system. A person without purpose is described as "spine less," "disjointed," "a puppet," and "dispirited."

The Alexander Technique taught that through awareness control and self-awareness development, body alignment improves. It focused attention on the relations between the head and the body because the head typically moves up from the top of the spine, and the back lengthens to relieve abnormal pressures upon it. Now relate this technique to what you learned about connective tissue. If you are unaware of what your body is telling you, if you are unaware of how you are moving your body, and unaware of how your body has been developing, you are going to have problems with the all important spinal cord. You can get a book teaching you the Alexander Techniques if you want to alleviate your back pain, be more passionate and spontaneous in your life, and have more self-control. These techniques promote excitatory and inhibitory self-control, self-awareness, and spontaneity, and a rewarding sense of lightness and freedom.

Another example of Alexander's techniques, mastery through surrender, is hard for people with controlling natures to understand. Being in the flow is described as when a person becomes *one* with whatever he is trying to do. Listen to a swimmer describe moving through the water effortlessly and literally having a sense of flow. A rider learns to move in perfect rhythm with his horse or his bicycle so that two are acting as one. When we surrender ourselves spiritually, mentally, and physically we are not constricted by anything, nothing holds us back, not even our thoughts. **We are simply being, which is the most effective use of our energies.**

The technique of Progressive Relaxation helps us focus on our spiritual alignment as it activates the emotions of our soul seat. We are connected to our soul seat through our heart. We speak of *"being at the heart of something,"* or we say, *"our heart is not in some-thing,"* because we know that the heart is where we feel. Edmund Jacobson, an American physician found that relaxation of our skeletal muscles helps us to control our emotions. Relaxation is what slows down our heartbeat. In a relaxed state people are able to become aware of their feelings and able to receive higher thoughts. Their peace and harmony is reflected in their faces and bodies. People who have found their higher self have physical and emotional calmness and control. A person engaged in the fulfillment of his spiritual longing has a vision and created image. Jacobson found that when we create images where the Creator's will and our own are in alignment, we create new sensorimotor skills of extraordinary states of consciousness through the creation of balance in our spirit-mind-body. Watch the graceful, flowing way a person walks who is, as we say, *in touch with themselves.*

To live optimally, a person's spirit-mind-body must have movement and energy. The body's movement keeps the connective tissues from becoming bonded and making it difficult to move. The muscles are relaxed and operating optimally. We can become stagnate in our bodies and in our minds. When we hold on to negative thoughts, the muscles tighten and become toxic. Those same toxic, negative thoughts produce mental and emotional illness.

We were taught that as we became adults the parts of our skull fused together. This is not true for people who are allowing their mental, physical and emotional energies to flow. The skull is alive and changing, and it responds to massage as much as any other part of our body. When we are rigid in our thinking, rigid in our movement, and emotionless, our skulls become hardened. Ever described someone as a rockhead? When we feel a passion for our purpose, and we give and receive love, we create energy in our spirit-mind-body in the same way that we create energy and well-being doing aerobic exercise, working hard, and stretching. Just as our connective tissues can become bonded, our mind and our thinking can become narrow and restrictive, and our emotions become shut off and unexpressive.

Our nervous system receives in going information, but it also sends outgoing information. Our nervous system first picks up information in the electromagnetic field. We've been around people and said that they sent a bad vibration or they a pulled energy out of our body. We can actually feel tension in the air. We have the same ability to send out positive or negative messages to the person standing next to us and even further out to the universe. It must be remembered that our spirit-mind-body works in an in going and out going fashion. Nothing about our spirit-mind-body is a one way street.

It is easy to see the physical connections in our body and to understand the importance of body alignment. Mental and spiritual alignment and connectedness are equally important.   We use our minds in the achievement of fulfilling our purpose and intention in life. Equally important is fulfilling our spiritual longing or passion in life. Our problems begin when we do not maintain balance physically, mentally, and spiritually.

You've met each of these types:

The person who thinks he is only body. He may spend all of his time exercising his physical body. Because he believes he derives his power from his body, he thinks only from the physical level. He spends no time on mental, emotional, or spiritual growth. He only sees himself as an earth being and never seeks higher levels.

A person who spends all their time in mental pursuit and neglects their physical side or spiritual side is equally unbalanced. Their neglected bodies and spirits are weakened. They are disconnected to the world and people.

We tend to put people who "live in the clouds" or "dwell mostly in the spiritual world" on a higher plane, and they do to. Yet they are as unbalanced as the other two types because they fail to remember that they live in the world. They fail to take responsibility for their purpose here on earth and lack a conscious awareness of what is going on around them.

The balanced person grows and develops in spirit-mind-body. This can be pictured as an equilateral triangle, the strongest form of building anything–architecturally or our bodies.

We have learned that **everything** in the universe is different forms of energy. When we can see ourselves as more than physical matter, then we can operate as energy beings. Our physical matter operates because of energy. The energy entering us, within us, and radiating from us manifests as **light** and **love.** When we are radiating anything other than light and love, it is because we are reacting to the external world. The first principal we must understand is that our minds and bodies are energy.

Light is everywhere and all around your whole body. Look at our language filled with light metaphors. When we understand something, we say the "light just came on," and "things are becoming clear." We say that people are luminous and shining. We describe great spiritual leaders as being "enlightened." On the physical level your body is making you anew changing your atoms, your cells, and tissues. Every cell in your body works through a process of positive and negative charges that produce both light and energy. Your body is covered mass and "appears" as dense matter, yet it is light, energy and love.

We are connected to the universe because we receive "enlivened energy" in different forms. Our bodies receive energy in the form of light, heat, and vibration. Our largest sensory organ, the skin, receives light-energy from the stars and the star closest to us, the sun. Ever tried to grow a plant without light or see a person locked up in a prison cell without light and you know its importance. Our own body energy rises in the spring with the increased light. Don't let the scare about skin cancer cause you to neglect your definite need for sunlight.

The Principle of Flow

The Principle of Energy described us as vibrational beings. In order to vibrate at a high level our bodies must be in alignment. This involves the sequential ordering of the circuits in the body and the pathways of the mind. First we are going to talk about energy being produced as thought and flowing through the muscles and the nerves or stored as negative energy. The body's metabolic energy systems are what I call *stars*. Their resonance, frequency, and vibration must be in agreement to be *open* and *allow energy to flow.*

The other part of alignment and flow is on the mental/ spiritual level. This is when spontaneously the person feels or experiences a connection with other people and energy flows between them. At other times people experience a pleasant state of being, or a feeling of oneness and attunement. I heard a woman at a dance say she would dance with a man while she unknowingly shook her head no. Her physical was not in alignment with her mental. By the way, this woman had a lot of back problems because she did not stand up for herself.

We know that energy flows through our glands, our nervous system and neurotransmitters. In this part of the book we are going to focus on how energy travels through our muscles. The question in the introduction, *"How do we do energy attunements and charge our circuitry system?"* is explained here in the section on muscles and also on the section on our nervous system because as we said, nerves travel through our muscles. We charge our circuitry system, negatively or positively, with mind energy, electrically and chemically, through our thoughts. This also answers the question,

"How do I remove constriction and operate in the zone?" We do it through our thoughts.

Pumping our muscles creates energy flow and is another way to remove constriction. Chronically tense and constricted muscles stop fluid circulation. We have nerves inside the cranium and the spine. All the other nerves are called peripheral nerves, the nerves supported by the body's muscles. When we don't use our muscles, the spaces around the nerves are not irrigated, which means that they are not nourished and waste is not removed. Axons are long, thin tubes which run in the middle of nerve cells. The flow of fluids that move through the axons keeps the proper conditions of the nerves' membranes and the propagation of actions potentials. This is the reason we get that sluggish feeling when we don't exercise, and we say our nerves are "on edge."

Muscle Basics

Muscle is a connective tissue.
Each muscle cell has only three options: it can
shorten (contract), it can lengthen, or it can lock in
place.

✴ **The body's muscles respond to everything happening to it internally and externally.**
✴ **Muscles change when thoughts (mind energy) are supported by feelings (emotions).**
✴ **Our muscles record our emotional thinking.**
✴ **Everything going on in the mind is expressed in muscular movements: muscle tenseness or relaxation, nervous actions such as finger tapping, and foot movement.**
✴ **Even the smooth muscles of the organs reflect our thoughts: expanding or contracting of arteries, flow of stomach juices, sweat glands, skin reactions such as flush or whiteness.**
✴ **The more substantial and similar to the desired movement the sensory memories are, and the clearer and more precise the image formed in the movement is, the more rapidly it will be mastered.**

Ideally our muscles should make up seventy to eighty-five percent of our body's weight. The abundance and scarcity of muscles, and the flaccidity or tension of our muscles define our size, our contours, our "feel" and the quality of all our physical actions. We describe strong muscular people as "standing their ground," of being firmly "planted." Watch the muscular movement, the walk, the posture and body language of the few super athletes and you can tell that they think differently and move differently from most people and even most athletes. All of their body muscles move with grace and flow. If you want to learn to move your body this same way, read on.

Muscles and The Fenn Effect

You've heard the statement "A little work never hurt anyone." Actually work can help the energy flow of your muscles and keeps them from atrophying. The Fenn Effect is based on the fact that when muscles perform work, they consume more oxygen and other nutrients. **Muscles in a state of sustained tension work against another muscle that is in a static position,** plus, they require more nutrition.

When our muscles are in sustained contraction, they reduce the circulation of oxygen and glucose by squeezing the small arteries and capillaries. Extended contraction of muscles reduces fluid circulation. Remember that holding on and staying attached to things, ideas and negative memories causes us to contract our muscles.

Now here's what we need to remember. *Muscle holding a chronic pattern of tension is working just as hard, and requires just as much metabolic support as does muscle that is exercising actively and getting work done.* In other words, it's taking up as much energy.

The Sol and Gel States of Muscles

Both muscles and connective tissues display a liquid crystal quality. When the muscles are completely relaxed, in a state of passive flaccidity, they are in the sol state. When they are hardened and flexed, they are in the gel state. Muscles are formed like long, thin, fine threads sometimes pliable and sometimes stiff. Fortunately, muscles can shift from sol to gel states almost instantaneously through thoughts becoming mind energy.

When we do not exercise the muscles, or when we use our mental energy to continuously tighten our muscles, they become hardened. The inside of a muscle is composed of extremely long molecules arranged in parallel. The molecules become stiff with **chemical bonding agents** because of three reasons: lack of physical exercise and relaxation, the production and transmission of negative hormones and chemicals from negative thinking, and the lack of openness on the mental level.

When we talked about the brain, we described it as a transformer for sensations that are constantly being flashed from the nervous system to the brain. The brain responds by connecting to information stored in it, so immediately a reaction takes place all over the body. We also talked about all of the muscles being connected so it is as if we only have one muscle. When a muscle receives an electrical or chemical energy message from the brain, the muscle impulsively shortens and contracts, thereby causing pressure on the nerves that pass through it. This is why we say that we feel a lot of mental and physical pressure and it's all happening at once.

If the muscles do not relax, excess tension remains in the muscles surrounding the nerve fibers. Ever been so nervous you said you felt like you could jump out of you skin? This prolonged contraction is at the base of nervousness. Nervous people are opening themselves up for disease. A person having a nervous breakdown is unable to function mentally and physically.

When a person is in a state of relaxation his large muscles and the other components of his body, such as blood pressure, pulse, respiration etc., his response to unexpected outside stimuli is handled with a sense of ease and calmness. Though he may cause an accident, this is the reason a drunk driver might not experience the physical injuries of the other people in the accident. There are certainly better ways of achieving relaxation through self-reflection, exercise, and self-relaxation exercises. An athlete who is relaxed isn't injured to the degree you think they would be. Watch a skier come tumbling down the steepest of hills with skis still attached and most don't break a bone because they relax through the fall.

Volition is a conscious choice about what we want to do. You can use volition to determine what your muscles do. This is what we do when we hit a perfect golf swing or the perfect homerun. You can watch a person's body and know the outcome without looking where the ball lands. We already watch athletes use guided imagery, physical practice, and their cognitive skills. Mental suggestion and verbal exhortations encourage many a player to extraordinary feats. We can use these same skills.

Muscles play a direct part in our conscious sensory experience. For example, if we experience the sensory experience of pain because of a wreck and we allow the muscle to constrict and hold on to the memory of the pain, not only the muscle will be affected, but the nerve tissue around the muscle will no longer transmit neural information. This translates into the nerve's inability to transfer energy that contains information about what we think and how we feel emotionally. We speak of people putting walls up, or people armoring themselves with their muscles. Ever tried to connect with a person who has "shut down?" They appear "dead" because the mental, physical and spiritual energy is stagnating. This is the reason that it is important for us to develop our sense of awareness about what is happening in us. The Principle of Awareness will be discussed later.

The facts:

* Muscles work together as whole units.
* Movement is organized in general shapes and directions and feelings.
* Our minds form the idea or the image or the feel of a movement.
* The idea, image or feeling memory then acts like a sensory engram directing the muscles as a whole.
* As an action is repeated, sensory feedback clarifies our finer details of the desired movement. The more specifically we can associate with the action the more accurately we can do it.

Any time the body has experienced trauma the muscles react by contracting. Something must be done to keep the muscle from staying in a state of contraction and to return to a relaxed state. The muscle will hold on to the memory of the trauma and hold on to toxic fluids. We to go to physical therapy after something traumatic, but unfortunately we deny our awareness of our emotional problems and don't spend time working them out. My personal belief is that hospitals should have massage therapists on staff. Nurses used to routinely massage patients as part of their healing. Massage creates the same effects as stillness and self-reflection. It does not matter whether we produce a state of an inner mental calm and allow its influence to project out into the muscles or whether we get a massage or exercise and thus induce a calmer inner state.

Moshe Feldenkrais, the creator of the Feldendrais Method, believed that humans could control their physical behaviors and responses. His acting career was interrupted because the muscles in his throat constricted and he couldn't speak. What set his methods apart was that he believed we achieve new awareness though movement that includes exercises in which limbs, head, neck, and torso are moved in **unaccustomed** ways. Let me suggest that you practice a different walk, a different posture, or a different way to hold your head. In viewing videos of my speaking, I noticed that I frequently hold my head to the left or right, throwing my body off center. Now I make a conscious effort to hold my head centered and in alignment.

Instead of being on automatic pilot Feldenkrais thought that we need to become self-aware so that we can freely determine our responses. Our goal should be that our responses are very highly articulated and the result of spontaneous action. How many times have you acted spontaneously and felt great? Spontaneity comes when you do not stop to access what you are or anyone else is going to think. Not placing judgment is freeing. A loss of spontaneity, not valuing your self worth, developing inhibitions against further learning, loss of awareness, and unnecessary limitations upon emotional and mental capacities, cause us to live in a state of atrophy. Feldenkrais believed that physical movement was the answer to atrophied abilities, and that movement stimulated further improvement by simultaneously cultivating sensation, emotions, thinking and motor activity. Many of us tend to stop learning when we have mastered sufficient skills to attain our immediate objective. Feldenkrais believed in the importance of hands-on bodywork that can produce a feeling of freedom, lightness and balance accompanied by new spontaneity and pleasure.

People who are nervous, bored, angry, and unhappy may eventually become ill. For many, illness turns out to be a blessing because it forces them to make changes in their lives. Elsa Gindler and Charlotte Selver developed a program teaching people how to heal themselves by encouraging kinesthetic sensitivity, play and openness. Elsa Gindler developed tuberculosis that caused her to look for ways to promote her body's natural restorative powers. She practiced sensitive attention to breathing, posture, and movement that formed the basis of her work. She came to see that calm in the physical field is equivalent to trust in the mental field. She taught the philosophy of Felassenheit, which means "allowing" or "letting go."

There is a direct connection of the pressures in your life to disease in your body. High blood pressure and circulation problems are cause by constricted capillaries, which supply the nutrition and carry off the waste products. At the same time, the contracting muscles are producing increased waste products and demanding increased nutrients from capillaries that are less able to supply them. This creates both an oxygen shortage and a waste build-up in the area, both of which are directly toxic to the nerve cells, irritate them, and contribute to even further muscular contractions. Additionally, chronically high levels of pressure upon nerve trunks are detrimental to their electrical activity (flow).

The following list is the price that we pay for *allowing ourselves to feel pressure*. In time, the results of these pressures can be the sharp ache of the sciatica nerve in our back, generated by the rotator muscles of the hip. Those of us who sit in front of a computer often experience numbness or tingling sensations in the hands from the neck muscles clamping down on the brachial plexus. My arms and hands would hurt so badly during the night I would rub and shake them vigorously trying to get the circulation moving again. Sitting in my desk chair in the same position caused my back muscles to constrict so I started getting massages. Also, I found a pressure point on my wrist and by simply adding pressure it sparked electrical energy. Chronic pains in the face and the head occur from pressure on the trigeminal nerve.

Strokes occur because the brain requires so much oxygen and blood to function. Smoking, bad eating habits, and stress cause constricted capillaries. We constrict our capillaries by holding in our emotions and by holding on to negativity just as much as we do by unhealthy behaviors and habits. Increasingly constricted capillaries require higher and higher blood pressure to make them function. Permanent damage occurs after they either collapse from the muscles squeezing them or burst from increased blood pressure because they will be replaced with scar tissue and not by new capillaries.

Every thought and every sensation finds expression in our systems through some modification of motor behavior, and every tension and every movement produces a sensory stimulation. We obtain sensory responses from touch receptors in the skin, pressure sensitive Pacinian corpuscles in deeper tissues, and Ruffini end organs in the joint capsules. What you need to remember from this information is that every distortion of tissue caused by muscular activity, from a tiny twitch in the corner of the eye to the full mobilization of the body in walking or running is in response to what we take in and how we choose to react. For example, if you came from a country that didn't have wasps and now you are in a place that does, you aren't going to react like I do when you see one. The mind can only relate to the things it already knows.

Achieving *flow* happens in spirit-mind-body only when we follow the universal principles we've been talking about—connection, balance, alignment, attunement, etc. The following are some steps you will need to take. First, you need to evoke a sensory memory. You've got to feel what it is that you want. Second, you need to release judgment on the outcome and on yourself. If you are thinking analytically or trying to control the thinking process, you are also stopping the flow of what will naturally be happening. You are limiting the outcome. Thirdly, you need to fix your imagination upon the goal so that you don't get off target for long. The good news is that you do not have to worry about the steps to get you to the goal. Our minds are created to work out the details once we know where we want to go.

The Body's Stars

Some time in elementary school we learned that we get energy from different sources. It is in the air that we breathe, the water we drink also contains oxygen, and the food that we eat contains nutrients. We are described as *dissipative structures* because of our continuous consumption of energy. But no one taught us about our having intake organs and glands that take in energy from the universal life energy field. The intake organs metabolize energy and send it to all parts of the body. Major nerve plexus are also located at these same places.

Our bodies are "open systems" meaning that we are involved in a continuous exchange and flow of energy. We are classified as *complex*, braided together beings. As complex structures we are connected at many points and in many ways. One place in our neck has twenty-one connection points. Because we are so complex, we need more energy to maintain all of our connections.

You will see a chart below that lists the "intake organs" or what I call "stars." If our "stars" are open, they will take in the right amount and right level of energy they need. In this case, the word **balance** means that our bodies are staying healthy by a **random** dispersal of energy. As energy beings we are always in a state of flux. The more connected we are, the more unstable our energies. This is what enables us to react quickly to danger or to be able to quickly achieve a relaxed state. Our ability to be flexible in our spirit-mind-body is that which keeps us healthy and energetic. For instance, we know that our mental energy and bodily functions slow down as we are sleeping. Otherwise, our minds would not go into delta states of deep sleep, or be relaxed enough to rest.

The following is a list of these intake organs that I call "stars" for the following two reasons: stars receive energy and they produce energy internally. Stars in the heavens and in our bodies send out heat, light, and energy.

Location	Endocrine Gland	Governing Area	Color
Base of spinal column	Adrenals	Spinal column, kidneys	Red
Sacral	Gonads	Reproductive system	Orange
Solar Plexus	Pancreas	Stomach, liver, nervous system, gall bladder	yellow
Heart	Thymus	Heart, blood, circulatory system, Vagus nerve	green
Throat	Thyroid	Bronchial and vocal apparatus Alimentary canal	blue
Head	Pituitary	Lower brain, left eye, ears, nose, nervous system	indigo
Crown of the head	Pineal	Upper brain, right eye	Purple-white

The chart shows what we call our body's seven levels of internal power and energy transformers. Each level of power is aligned to a physical system within the body. The amount of energy we take in and send out relates to the external and internal issues of our lives. For instance, what if you believe that a supervisor who primarily thinks negatively or who is only critical takes your power from you when they manage employees. Then, if you permit it, your energy level will be lower. We describe such people as being a pain. They are, and it manifests in our backs. If we feel powerless internally to change what is going on in our lives, we will limit our energy.

The seven levels of our energy body are expert record keepers of all the details of our lives. They determine how we distribute our life force. Remember that all of our cells have memory. For instance, if you had an overbearing father, and you are still grappling with that issue, you have a sense of powerlessness. Your third star, your solar plexus, the place where your internal strength is derived, will be weak. You will think that your power is external, and you will continue to be reactive to the events that happen in your life. Paying attention to our star energy system gives us a sense of a person's attitude toward life in the present and how our past has affected us. By reading a person's stars we can understand the person's basic emotional character.

After we have experienced an accident both our bodies and our minds react to a similar set of circumstances, whether there is a real danger or not. We say we're "gun shy." This intimate record keeping is good and bad. We can decide to never do something again because of real or unreal fears. Or, we can choose to overcome our fears and be conscious of our ability and power to use our energies forcefully.

The following is a short summary of the activities of each of the "stars."

The First Star

Our first star is located at the base of our spine in the perineal floor and is associated with the anus and the coccyx. Called the root star, it is related to protective strength and endurance of the father. The earth and the earth's energy is described as feminine. People with an open first star have feet that are grounded. They are linked to the actual energy of the earth and feel physically being a part of the grand universe of life. It makes sense that when parents make the child feel safe and grounded, they feel physically stronger and more connected to the earth. The adrenal glands, where we get strength in times of emergency, the kidneys and the bladder are associated with the first star. During these times abundant energy flows from the root into the legs and feet. We even describe a person who always seems to survive as "able to land on his feet." People whose first star was not fully developed constantly feel fear and lack vitality, radiance, and tenacity in life.

Sometimes we describe people as not being "grounded." We say that "their head is up in the clouds," or we say, "they are out in space." We tell them that they need to come down here on earth. Their lack of connection causes unbalance in spirit-mind-body. They have problems manifesting in the physical world and they can not make things happen, as they would like. While they may be creative, their efforts are blocked and frustrated because they can not put them into action.

The color associated with the first star is red, the color of passion. A strong and positive connection to the first star's energy is essential to our health because we are energy beings. Our physical bodies produce and thrive on electrical currents that, in turn, connect us to the physical life patterns of the earth.

On the other hand, we say that our ideas have taken root. When you sink your roots into the world, you are nurtured and nourished. You become more alive and animated. Your body's energy circuits are making contact with everything that is significant and precious to you. You actually feel that connection with all your senses, and you direct your energy to extend out from your system to connect with and be recharged by everything that you are holding in your mind and heart. When we forget the things that are important to us, we feel disconnected because the energy is not flowing through us.

The Second Star

The second star is located in the pubic area over the genitals and bladder area. It is associated with the color orange. This energy system is developed between the ages 7 to 14. When natural sexual development is blocked, the joy of sexuality and all of our other creative impulses is prohibited. Creativity takes passion. This is the energy center where we feel a magnetic attraction of others to us and us to them. This is where we've felt the "chemistry" for our partners. We attract people on our same vibrational level. If you don't like what you are attracting, you will first have to change yourself.

Centered at our sexual organs, the second star activates our sexual desires. On the other hand, it alerts us to dangers we cannot physically see and, when necessary, provides us with a degree of physical strength that courageously helps us protect ourselves. People are encouraged to listen to their sense of intuition that tells them to get away from a person who is about to harm them. We have to ability to feel a person's bad intentions.

We block the energy of this star when we have feelings of aggression, hostility, vengeance, or greed. How could you express loving energy when these thoughts are consuming you? A person who is intending betrayal, physical violence, or sexual abuse, holds negative thoughts and memories in their brain and the other cells in his body. This state of mind can produce several areas of dysfunction, including impotence. These people may become unable to maintain a vibrational link to those with whom they have personal relationships. Their energy is actually being drained faster than it can be replenished, a consequence of our obsession with negative thoughts. This is the reason you can look into the eyes of someone in depression, or about to do harm, and know how they feel or what they are going to do.

Third Star

This star is the location of your solar plexus—the center of your being—the location of your physical strength. A person who is not connected with the center of their being lacks personal power, a sense of self, the ability to be assertive. Learning to set your boundaries, of what is permissible and not permissible for other people to do to you, is so important. It is related to how you value yourself. Children who grow up with weak parental relationships never develop strong relationships with others. However, these people can enact their own mothering and fathering qualities. The third star is the "emotional mind," that place where one identifies with others. They can love themselves as their parents should have and they can teach themselves the *way of the world,* as the father should have. When a person has their basic needs met, they are able to be more effective and freer to be assertive.

The third star is associated with the color yellow, and it is the location of our core being. Energy is sent and received from the pancreas, an endocrine gland, also the stomach, liver, nervous system, and gall bladder. Its location is the navel, where martial artists and people who perform extraordinary feats of power go to get their strength.

Fourth Star

The fourth star is located over the chest, between the breasts. It is the connection between the lower three stars and the upper three stars. We know that the heart is where we find true self-love and true love for others. The joy that we find in life and our individual expression result in our ability to know our selves as truly loving, courageous, compassionate, and as an expression of our Creator. A strong fourth star says that we have come from being totally ego based and we are striving to become whole and integrated within.

Energy from the heart is sent down through a person's arms and legs. When we open our arms and hearts to another person, we are sending and wrapping around them our energy. The fourth star sends and receives green light, a physical and emotional healing color. Green represents new growth.

Fifth Star

The fifth star is located in the throat and it is where we speak our truth. We find that our emotions are more related to the lower stars but the fifth star is where we speak from the heart, where we express our emotions. We take our words and express the feelings of our heart and our compassion. Through our voice we express our creativity.

The emotions that we hold in our throat are the loud expressions of shouting, sobbing and screaming. When we hold back our expression, sometimes in the form of our anger, our throat becomes red. We swallow down anger and choke down our sorrows.

A woman whose entire neck was red explained that she felt she never spoke her truth. She never correlated her red neck with holding back anger. Anger held back in the neck is connected with the muscles of the shoulders and the large areas of the back. In reading a person's body language you will see a red-faced person with a thick short neck is a person who has constricted their words, or not *stuck their neck out.* They have pulled their shoulders up in rejection of responsibility. The fifth star is represented by the color blue. When we speak our truth, it gives us a sense of peace and comfort.

The Sixth and Seventh Stars

The sixth and seventh stars are concerned with our mental and spiritual natures rather than our emotional natures. **When we are in *higher states of consciousness,* we are not influenced by the electro-chemical activity of our body. We are influenced by higher states.**

The sixth star is located in the middle of the forehead. When we are in states of consciousness, the right and left brain hemispheres are working as integrated and whole. When we are comprehending holographically and seeing the whole truth, we are using our sixth star. It is the seat of true intelligence and the essence of things. As all the other five stars come together as one, the sixth star is called the mind's eye and the unified eye. It is the place where we perceive the *unseen, or when we are able to see all things clearly.* The sixth star sends out and receives purple light, which is associated with being on a spiritual level. A church I attend bought a pulpit from another church. You could see purple light shining from the pulpit because it retained the energy of the ministers who had been speaking at the other church.

The Seventh Star

The seventh star is located at the crown of the head. When a person experiences "union with the Divine," and " oneness with his Creator," he experiences a rare state of bliss. Many great authors such as Whitman, Blake, and Descartes had such an experience. In the beginning of this book I spoke of a funnel of white light entering the top of the head. You can see it, as they say, "as plain as day." Again, if you doubt this talk to nurses who help with delivering babies. A nurse told me of a baby whose delivery was difficult and the baby had not started breathing yet. The doctor eventually was able to get the baby to breathe, and at that moment, white light entered through the top of the baby's head. Nurses who serve the dying will tell you of seeing a white light exiting the body at the same time a person dies. Remember, energy is always in flux and is never destroyed.

The Seven Levels of the Electromagnetic Field

I've been teaching classes on different subjects all my life. My favorite class is teaching people about seeing their aura or the electromagnetic field and teaching them what the colors mean. I don't do it as a parlor game or to impress people that it takes any special ability. If you doubt that you have an electromagnetic field or that light is shining from you called an aura, I suggest again that you go look at the pictures in your Bible and see the halos of Jesus and Mary.

Mary was a human just as you and I are so I fail to see how people can think that there is anything supernatural about having or talking about auras. Jesus told us to let our light shine and not to put our light under a bushel. The only people who are not able to see auras are people who believe that they can't. Some people can see auras with their eyes shut, using their "third eye." Others actually feel different colors and are more sensitive to auras that way. Currently UCLA is doing research and studies on the aura.

To be able to see an aura is not hard. Children draw people with colored light around them until some poorly informed parent or teacher scares them about something perfectly normal. In my classes I teach people that they can change the color of their aura by what they thinking and feeling. They have visual proof of how our thoughts second by second affect us. I have stood before audiences and chosen to think loving thoughts or thoughts of a loved one and been told that not only is my aura is pink, but also my face became very soft and my body relaxed. Want to soften your wrinkles? Think loving thoughts.

Once a man at a conference asked me to look at his aura. As he **looked** (gave his full attention) to the speaker, I could see yellow light above his head, representing his rational, logical mind at work. When he turned his head, I could tell that he was immediately thinking about something else because his aura became a dark red. During the break I told him what I saw. He asked me to explain the colors. The dark red I told him was a sign that he was angry. He quickly said, "Oh, I am angry, *very angry*."

During another class the participants did a relaxation exercise and then a meditation. We could feel the spiritual energy in the room. The participants were invited to view the aura of the person opposite them and everyone in the class had purple light around them. The color purple is used in our religious practices because it represents the spiritual. It vibrates at the highest frequency of colored light.

The Seven Levels of the Electromagnetic Field

1. Physical Sensation

2. Emotions, with respect to self

3. Rational mind

4. Relations with others

5. Divine will within

6. Divine love, spiritual ecstasy

7. Divine mind, serenity

Level One

Level One of the electromagnetic field of a person appears as a bright white light if they are healthy. I was visiting a friend right after she had finished teaching a one-hour aerobic class and the white light around her extended three times as far as most people. A reporter said that while doing a video interview of Mother Teresa the electricity went off and the room became dark. He continued asking her questions and noticed that powerful white light surrounded her body. It also showed up on the videotape though the room was still dark. If you look into the viewfinder as you video someone, you will also see white light around them. People in my audiences tell me that my light grows brighter as I speak. Since speaking is one of my passions, I actually feel more energy after I stand on my feet and speak for an hour than when I began.

Freud said that the suppression of our emotions manifests as illness somewhere in the body. A friend of mine is a perfect example because she has created diabetes. Linda made the decision four years ago to do as little as possible. She ignored fulfilling her life's purpose and decided to lie in bed most of the day and watch TV. I can barely see light around Linda's body because she is utilizing so little energy and she has suppressed her emotions. She continued her habits of not exercising, and living on diet drinks and never drinking water, and not expressing her true feelings. Her quick answer to everything is to take a pill that then causes some bad side effect. Linda does not like change, and her mind is closed to new thoughts. The result of all of this is that she has gone from a size 12 to a size 3X. I wrote earlier how our posture reflects our attitude toward our lives and back problems result from our holding on to things. Linda's posture was always bad, but now she is bent over and suffers back problems. A side note, diabetes is a disease that causes the body to lose feeling. What we do with our minds and emotions also becomes manifest in the physical body.

Level 2

We reveal our emotions on the second level. A TV interview was done with a Mafia boss in jail for the rest of his life after personally killing or ordering the killing of thirty-four people. He expressed deep sorrow that he would never be with his family. Tears rolled down his cheeks, and you could see his face soften as he talked about all that he would miss.

The interviewer asked him how he felt about the families of the thirty-four victims he had murdered. His face hardened, his eyes became distant and glazed, and he replied matter-of-factly, "I didn't know any of those people, so I can't feel sorry for them."

Many people experience things so horrible or do things so horrible that they able to shut down their emotions and feelings about the event. However, shutting off our feelings has a heavy price. A mother, whose eighteen-year old son was killed in a fight, chose to forgive the other boy involved. He was sentenced to life in prison, but the mother visits and writes him. Her statement about her ability to forgive him is, "If I didn't forgive him and carried hate inside of me, I would go mad."

If you see yellow light on the second level, it means that the person is a loving and compassionate. When I speak to nurses, I see a room full of yellow light. The person who is nicknamed "Sunshine" is the one who makes us feel good, who gives us more energy just by being around them.

Level Three

The third level deals with the mental and rational world. The light on this level is very bright and full when we are using our full mental capacities. Our thoughts have a sense of clarity, a sense of appropriate-ness. We all spend a lot of our time in the mental world; the difference is hopefully that we don't spend all of our time there. We've all got a friend who seems to know information about most things, a whiz on the computer, but you would never asked him to play tennis or expect him to get passionate about sending aid to Turkey after the earthquakes.

You can tell when someone is thinking because the light above the head is yellow. This is not to be confused with the meaning of the yellow light on the second level. All of our thinking can be strictly mental, or our thinking can be raised to a higher spiritual level by receiving energy from divine mind, love, and will. We call this kind of thinking holistic because is creative, inspiring, and based on fulfilling purpose. Holistic thinking, or integrative thinking, is the integration of both sides of the brain. It is able to differentiate what is true and what isn't so that we can perceive with clarity. When the third level lacks balance, a person's thinking become narrow-minded and irrational.

Level Four

The introduction to this book talks about there being only one energy in the world. The people, animals, plants, inanimate objects, the earth, the sun, the stars, and the universe as a whole are a part of this one energy. The third principle in this book deals with connection with all the things listed above and the connection of everything within their systems.

If all this sounds too ethereal, let me make it appear more real. Have you seen one person send their energies across the room to another person? Are there certain people you choose to be around because the more inter-action you have with them, the more your own energy level increases? This is the reason that we stay healthier just by having pets around and why we get happier being out in nature or around other people. Level four is filled with several different colors of light that shoot out from the body. They look like the Christmas lights that we put on our houses that appear to be *running in narrow streams of color.* I met a woman and related to her immediately. We enjoyed talking on a deep level for a couple of hours. When I went home, I was still feeling the glow of our conversation. As I glanced in the mirror, I saw all different colors of light shooting out around my body. It was sort of scary at first because I had never seen this happen before. Another good friend and I relate so well that you can see different colored light around us when are together.

Levels Five, Six and Seven

This is not the book to discuss these levels in detail. Level five deals with divine will, level six deals with divine love, and level seven deals with divine mind. These levels deserve full discussion in a book solely about auras. They are not visible to most people.

The Principle of Non-Judgment

> Any belief system will make a person "set" to notice events and facts that support their belief and miss those that do not. Peter Russell

What does our being judgmental have to do with our level of energy? It has everything. When you are "being who you are," you are coming from a place of love and wisdom. The question in the introduction, **"How can I connect to right action,"** is answered that you can do nothing else when you are being wisdom and love. The second part of the question, **"How can I focus my energy to meet my goals?"** receives the same answer. After you clear your thinking and memories, learn to be still and receive intuitive information, remove attachments and judgments. There is no other place to focus your energies but on goals and purpose. Go back to the fact that you can only think of one thing at a time. If you are using your thoughts to place judgment, then you are not creating new ideas. Judgment is not just placed on past events, but we also place judgment on future events. When we do that, we place a limit on what can happen.

When we place a judgment on something, we are doing three things. First, we are using mind energy just to think about it. Second, we are placing a value on it. Third, by putting energy into it and placing a value on it, we then become tied to it. The result is that the idea, thing, or person also has a hold on us. To be able to look at **anything** without judgment is to let it be.

Non-judgmental thinking is a transforming philosophy of clear thinking. What percentage of your thought is wasted on being judgmental? Would you say the result is low energy? Napoleon Hill stated it succinctly, ***"If you continue to think the way you have been thinking, you will get what you have been getting."***

Clear, non-judgmental thinking promotes the most productive, creative, and resourceful problem solutions. It enables you to envision an absolute expectation that what you are going to do is going to work. It determines your success in all relationships, time management, focus, direction, and business acuity.

Bringing to mind the word CLEAR will help you stay open to new thoughts, help you focus your "light," so that you can direct your intention and attention.

C-control
L-light
E-energy
A-awareness
R-respect

When we stay tied to old judgmental thinking patterns, we continue to use energy depleting behaviors about learned helplessness, being either a martyr or victim, and blaming others. Did you ever see a martyr or a victim with a lot of energy? Nope. It takes a lot of energy to constrain our selves. Even the martyr spends a lot of their energy controlling the other person. Blaming others is what we are talking about, placing judgment. What we are doing is voluntarily relinquishing our control to the other person. This allows them to be in charge of our energies. Wouldn't you prefer to develop a sense of control, power, and purpose in your life? Wouldn't it be better to find your own vision and to find the answer to achieving meaningful and successful relationships?

What if you applied clear, non-judgmental thinking to:

♦ **Utilize your intuitive abilities to be a creative thinker.**

We waste a lot of energy telling people and ourselves what we can not do instead of focusing on what we can do. Frequently when I speak I mention that a lot of people know on their wedding day that they are making a mistake. During the breaks people come up and tell their stories.

One woman said, "My Daddy turned to me before we went down the aisle and said, 'You don't have to do this if you don't want to. We can stop right here.' I lied, and said that I loved the guy I was going to marry. Besides, I thought, all those people are waiting."

Another woman said she knew she was making a mistake and cried all the way down the aisle! I always ask them how many years did it cost you not to listen to your intuition? One woman replied, "Twelve unhappy years and two unhappy children." Another common reply is "I thought," some say hoped, "that it would work out." My next question is "Did you know that it wouldn't work out?" and they always say, "Yes, I realize now that knew I was making a mistake."

The initial problem is that both the bride and the groom judged themselves not worthy of happiness or love. Mistakes people make in their lives because they do not listen to their intuition are the cause of their depression, lack of focus, and lack of passion that can all be bundled under lack of energy. We bring our home-life to work with us every day and share it through our electromagnetic field.

♦ **Stop group, mass conscious thinking**

Mass conscious thinking has ridiculed every new idea and thought. As you read the biographies of all the great thinkers, you will see that mass conscious thinking has placed judgment on all new thought from visionaries such as Jesus, Einstein, Gandhi, and Newton. What we can learn from these people is to look at what we believe that is mass conscious thinking and decide whether it is true, or just what everyone believes to be true.

♦ **Focus your gifts, talents and abilities to become a better employer, employee and person.**

Worrying about the judgments that others will place on us stifles our energies because we are not focusing on being. When I started out as a speaker I knew that I had a desire to speak, but I didn't really have an area of expertise. Like a lot of speakers, I told my personal story. I took the same path as most speakers, billing myself as able to speak in several different areas. As I moved along my journey of study and self-study, I would write in the margins, energy is what I want to talk about. As I look back now, I see that all the steps were part of the process. Many times in a state of confusion about my direction, I asked other people what they thought I should do. The replies were always from their experiences and perspectives, of course. My initial reaction would be anger because they didn't know what I believed that I should be doing. What did I expect? I had asked them to make their truth mine. I was not spending my energy on believing what only I knew were my individual gifts, talents, and abilities. Consequently I quit asking other people to place a judgment or an opinion on what I should be doing.

♦ **Become open, aware and embrace the differences in personalities and individuality.**

We spend a lot of energy trying to remake people to be just like us. Do you cringe like I do when you hear the media talk about us as ordinary people? We are all extraordinary. People who have done a lot of self-study and reflection can tell you their true individual character traits, the things that make them uniquely individual. These traits were given to them to express through their energies. We are not talking about *focusing* on outward appearance expression, but expression of individuality from the inside out. Our appreciation of the difference in others stems from the appreciation of our own differences.

What You Will Gain From Non-Judgmental Thinking

We've all done and seen the success of brain storming. One of the rules is that you present ideas without judging whether they will work or not. Why not put your mental energies into individual brain storming? Instead of re-circulating the same old ideas around in your head, most of which are about why things won't work or can't be done, why not create new solutions to the challenge?

Our self-imposed humps in the road are that we don't believe that we have the ability or the internal resources to think up something totally new and different. Secondly, we believe that one person can not use their mental energy to create a new reality. Thirdly, we do not know the power in getting other people with like minded thoughts and energy to join us in our affirmations. A few people focusing their energy on positive results can overcome a mass of people with negative energies simply because they are vibrating at a higher energy level. It begins by transforming and recreating a new you in creating, leading, teaming, communicating and relating to others. We say it all the time, "We're working on a different level."

Raising our energies to higher levels teaches us how to premeditate our actions and make great decisions. We get the consistency in life that we've always wanted, because we have learned how to retain our power and control in every situation.

Characteristics of Clear Thinkers

They believe in an unlimited world.

They know and value their self worth.

They focus on doing the best with their abilities rather than competing with others.

They spend time looking within to discover their gifts, talents, and abilities.

They look at the bigger picture rather than at small setbacks.

They surround themselves with positive people who are like- minded.

They use imagery and affirmations to secure a positive and productive future.

They see beyond the physical world.

They are trendsetters instead of followers.

They realize that their energy will follow their attention.

Their main concern is:

To speak directly and honestly, telling the truth rather than what people hope they will hear.

To achieve great results rather than worrying about mistakes.

To face confrontations which are necessary and lead to personal growth.

To change their lives because it is necessary to fulfill their purpose.

To act more directed and stay focused.

To avoid dangerous situations and people who will take their energy.

The Principle of Awareness

AWARENESS: THE FIRST STEP OF
ACCOUNTABILITY, ACTIVITY, AND
ACHIEVEMENT

Give Yourself the "Awareness Test"

* Have you written your autobiography? Have you looked at the patterns in your life?
* Have your recalled what you liked to play as a child?
* Are you willing to enhance yourself by going within?
* Have you looked at your thinking, emotional and behavioral patterns?
* Do you realize that you are able to change the course of your existence by taking time to think?
* Do you feel that you have balance in your life?
* Do you feel that you need more energy?
* Do you lack focus and attention?
* Are you aware of who you really are?

"Only awareness, which has nothing to do with mental activity, which is free from all reference to the past, free from bodily and psychological habits, free from selection and repetition, can open the door to spontaneous understanding."—*Jean Klein*

Awareness is living in the present moment and is the means to help us achieve our desired state of being. It is the pathway to the wisdom of our minds. Awareness is the key to success in our health problems, relationship problems, and emotional problems. Our compassion and productivity is increased through our awareness of our emotions.

Every thought and sensation finds a way of expression in our body. Following this, every tension and every movement produce a sensory stimulation. As a result of our false or negative ideas and thoughts, our bodies become distorted and stressed. In response, our bodies turn off their awareness (consciousness.)

* **You must be aware of your individuation**
* **You must be aware of your differentiation**
* **You must seek integration**
* **You must seek clarity**

When we are irresponsible, we are choosing to be unaware of the feelings, needs, desires of others.

Have you ever been to a battlefield site, a prison, fort, concentration camp, anyplace where there was a lot of killing? I visited a Civil War fort outside Savannah, Georgia and had a unique experience feeling the energies of a place. I felt a soldier's fear during battle. People who have visited concentration camps in Germany say that they can still smell blood. Of course, the actual blood is gone but the memory is still held there through the energy. Some say that smell is the most powerful sense energetically. Aromas instantly translate into emotions stored in your memory.

You may have an antique piece of furniture that contains a lot of positive or negative energy. All objects are heard, seen, felt, and smelled simultaneously. Take a moment to unfocus your eyes and look at a picture that hangs on an off-white wall. In a few seconds colored light appears that reflects the energy of the person who lives there. Most of the time my aura is green, and the energy in my furniture, pictures, actually everything in my house, emits green light.

You can check your clothing the same way. Everything around us picks up our smells and our energy. My first encounter was seeing green light shining from my favorite pink terrycloth robe lying on the bathroom counter. The color also showed in the mirror behind the counter. You may have had the desire to wear the clothing of someone you love. Their loving energy in the clothing gives you a sense of comfort. If this sounds a bit much, then you are the kind of person who would buy a house near power lines because you can't see or feel all the energy overload the lines are sending out.

Anne Sullivan, Helen Keller's teacher, said Helen was able to distinguish with great accuracy the different undulations of the air and the vibrations of the floor made by various sounds and motions. She was able to recognize her friends the instant she touched their hands or clothing. Helen Keller could determine a person's mood by the slightest emphasis placed upon a word, a change in position, and the varied play of the muscles of the hand.

The Principle of Focused Attention

Focused attention is achieved through meditation, self-reflection, visualization, relaxation, breathing in colors, selecting peaceful feeling states, and recovering information from the unconscious. All of the above are answers to the question in the introduction, *"How can I sustain energy levels?"*

If you asked most people to describe the state of their lives, you would receive comments such as...

"I feel like the internal dialogue in my mind is really a committee of idiots."

"I'm under so much pressure at work. There are times I have to hide out in my office and sit quietly to keep from feeling that my heart is exploding."

"I was out of the office for just two days and I had 80 E-mail messages. All this technology was supposed to make things easier for us but now everyone expects an immediate answer. Everything has a sense of emergency. It is as if no one can think for himself. Everyone in our office is so fearful of losing their jobs, they spend most of their time trying to look busy and in charge, while in reality, no one is doing any thinking."

"I'm like everyone else, suffering from information overload, and yet, I don't know how to find out the answers to the really important questions. All I really want is peace of mind, but I don't know where to get it."

If you asked someone, "Would you like to have bliss, inner harmony, and centeredness in your life?" could you imagine anyone saying, "No?" Then ask what they are doing to achieve these things. Most people will say, "very little."

Self-reflection and meditation is the only way to find and connect to the peace within. It is found when we learn to control our mental and emotional bodies and stay centered within. We say we believe the statement, "peace can never be found or experienced outside of oneself," and yet, we take no action to find peace. Meditation teaches us how to master this state of mind and once we do we discover who we really are.

You can have peace of mind and harmony in your life. And it is available to all. But there are some requirements to be a successful meditator. First, meditation is based on personal experience. You can't just read about it or buy it in a package. Meditation is one of those, "individually responsible," acts that requires us to do something so many of us deem hard today. Meditation requires that we still our minds through a discipline of "relaxed concentration."

Purification of the mind is not done through thinking. You have to meditate. This is when your mind has no particular thoughts; it is in a state of pure awareness. You allow yourself simply to be. Meditation gives you inner growth where you reach an expanded state of mental and spiritual development. It helps you get rid of old thought patterns and rigid habits of thinking and feeling. This kind of thinking is what is making you depressed and have low energy. They are distractions from reality. Look at where your thoughts come from now? They *can* come from a place of peace and silence—within. This can be your reality.

What can you achieve through meditation? Well, how would you benefit or enjoy a life of increased personal control over the mind and the emotional and physical functions.

Write down any challenges or concerns that you are having right now and you will find that they will fall into one of three categories. We all want to improve our health, have better relationships, and enjoy the job where we probably spend most of your time?

After you read the following information about what meditation can do for you, hopefully, you will be saying to yourself this is the key to everything. How do I go about it?

Meditation is a practice of constant observation of the mind. **Most of the time, we are focusing on our thoughts rather than simply focusing on the mind.** The benefit of focusing on one point or object is to still the mind in order to perceive our true self. So, what's so wonderful about knowing one self? The access to your mind enables you to obtain the wisdom for dealing with every aspect of your life and therein lies your tranquility.

Most of us have difficulty with the simple act of concentration for more than a few seconds. Meditation is the next step past concentration. It might take you a half an hour to achieve a state where your body and mind transcend to a level of total unity. But the power of that two and a half minutes, when you are in a true meditative state, will give you a great sense of purpose and strength like you have never experienced. Your ability to think and concentrate will radically magnify.

The sense of peace that meditation brings your life can be compared to a visit to a lake whose surface is as smooth as a thin layer of ice. Most of the time our lives are like living on a beach near an ocean. Huge waves of sensory input disturb our minds. There is a never-ending splash of sounds, smells, and feelings entering the ocean of our mind. When we are at the ocean, we observe the power of the external world. Thoughts and desires are constantly crashing into us.

In order to feel the power of our internal world, we must go to a place of peace and quietness like the tranquil lake. When we enter that space, we can relax in the present moment of joy and peace.

What you are doing for that moment in time is stepping back and simply observing yourself—your mind. Instead of identifying with your emotions, thoughts, and actions, you are on the other side of the camera—a silent observer. You pass no judgment—good or bad. Your thoughts become powerless over you. As the cameraman, you begin to control your thoughts and emotions. You can observe and simply register them on the film or you can make them grow smaller or larger. You can illuminate the thoughts and feelings you choose. You can roll the film backward or forward. You can freeze a frame, edit, or splice it. You have control of everything! Learning to be a cameraman takes time and attention, so does the training of your mind to be in meditation.

Stillness and Self-Reflection Promotes Health

* Stress reduction
* Pain reduction
* Treatment of depression, anxiety, and irrational fear
* Lowering blood pressure and heart rate
* Decreasing medications, lowering cholesterol
* Decrease in rate of breathing
* Strengthen your self-discipline to achieve your weight and exercise goals

Mental and Emotional Well-being

* Renewing and controlling your thinking
* Achievement of clear thinking by slowing brain waves
* Developing healthy emotional responses
* Transforming your life and achieving balance, harmony and synergy
* Acquiring new skills
* Changing negative habits and behaviors
* Changing your unhealthy thought patterns
* Succeeding with self-help programs
* Increasing your creativity and decision-making skills
* Fulfilling your purpose in life, becoming more productive and successful

---

Create the mentally, physically, and emotionally healthy life you desire by using the right hemisphere of your brain. Fill your life's journey with peak experiences.

How to Still Your Mind Energy

The TV news report just discussed another success of Neuro-Feedback. Children with autism, dyslexia, attention deficit and other learning problems are taught to do Neuro-feedback playing a game on their TV screen using their mind energy. Neuro-feedback also works for adults who want to increase their ability to concentrate and remember. The good news is you can already do Neuro-feedback by just practicing focused attention.

To know why is it important for us to keep our bodies in a state of relaxation, we must consider the following statement. *It is not the events that happen to us that affect our reaction. It is our attitude.* We gain a new perspective of life when we realize that distress is self-activating. We can learn to act more calmly and efficiently in all our circumstances.

When a person is in a state of relaxation, his large muscles and the other components of his body, such as blood pressure, pulse, respiration etc., respond to unexpected outside stimuli with a sense of ease and calmness. We previously referred to Progressive Relaxation, developed by American physician, Edmund Jacobson. It enlists our natural capacities for self-regulation through simple contraction and relaxation of particular muscles by focusing attention on specific body parts and by articulating our capacity for selective control.

Jacobson's work indicated that mental events unrelated to external stimuli are often accompanied by muscular contractions. He observed the facial expression and postural changes exhibited by subjects engaged in mental imagery. Mental images are usually accompanied by subtle eye movements and small muscular contractions of the forehead, tongue, torso, and limbs. When a person is not telling the truth, the iris of his eyes becomes smaller. People give off other signals that they are lying. Muscles in their faces twitch, they avoid eye contact, and their hands sweat. The studies showed that unnecessary movements can be diminished, or even eliminated, through relaxation. Taking increasing responsibility for all our functioning, we can respond to the environment's demands with an even temper. We've all seen an emotionally agitated person pace around a room as a means to relax his muscles. This gives him the ability to control his emotions.

Jacobson showed that muscular tensions exhibited by knitted brows or postural rigidity predisposed his subjects to experience a pronounced startle response. Relaxed subjects, on the other hand, do not react to potentially jarring stimulation with such strong contractions. Jacobson found that muscles already contracted were more likely to contract further in response to an unexpected stimulus.

Want to work with greater efficiency, mentally and physically? Physical relaxation reduces tension, and thereby, wear and tear on your body and mind. Many companies have exercise rooms but if you aren't able to get to one you can send the message to relax to your body. In the same way mental images produce relaxation in our faces, foreheads, eyes, mouths, torso, and arms and legs, physical relaxation enables us to breeze through life's activities.

Our bodies were designed for self-regulation because our nervous system is in every part of our body. Equally important, we have the ability through self-awareness and conscious volition to control our attitudes.

People in all professions, from. ballet dancers, singers, to salesmen, know that they perform better when they are relaxed. Relaxation frees us from distracting thoughts or feelings, decreases distracting movements which improves our ability to focus and concentrate.

Stillness, Self-reflection and Autonomic Response

Through stillness, self-reflection and yoga we can achieve certain states of mind and physical postures that give us control over the healthy functioning of internal organs and glands. Visceral muscles and even the blood chemistry are verifiably affected when we still the mind and stretch the body. Meditation produces consistent shifts in many of the body's internal activities, such as, slowing the heart rate and respiratory rate, with the direct result that the body's use of oxygen and the production of carbon dioxide drops, indicating an overall reduction in the rate of metabolism. The people I have met with high blood pressure say that their doctor just prescribes blood pressure medication. I ask them if they know the benefits of meditation and many reply that it is easier to just take two little pills. They do not take the time to find to cause of their high blood pressure or all the benefits of meditation.

During self-reflection an increase in blood flow to the muscles can be observed, stepping up oxygenation even though the breath and heartbeat have slowed down. The level of lactate in the blood is reduced. This is a chemical process that produces a toxic waste product—lactate. Injections of lactate into a normal person typically causes local pain and acute mental anxiety. There is also a measurable increase in the electrical resistance of the skin.

Self-reflection produces a range of symptoms which are complementary opposites of the body's responses to pain or stress, **lowering its metabolic activity and its muscle tone (and hence its expenditure of energy) while thought processes remain at a conscious and alert level.**

Technique # 1 Focused attention

This state can be described as nearly cataleptic. During focused attention a person may endure discomfort and the forgetfulness of pain. The TV show 20/20 did a video of a woman who was having laser surgery done on her face without anesthetics. A hypnotist put her into a focused state so that she wouldn't feel pain. During the surgery, she started coming out of the state but just a few words from the hypnotist put her back into the state.

Another TV show did a story about two women who were about to have natural childbirth. Both went to a doctor who taught a series of classes on hypnosis. Though both woman had very long labors, both were able to keep themselves into a hypnotic state and not experience child birthing pain. This seems the most reasonable thing in the world to me and it makes you wonder why all doctors don't use hypnosis. Another advantage of hypnosis is that the bodies of both women were so relaxed that after childbirth they were able to get up and walk around. Athletes many times do self-hypnosis and are able to perform even with their bodies hurting. Many writers are able to produce more creative work in a state of relaxation. We've seen people or experienced times when we were so absorbed in an analgesic state or had selective amnesia.

Stillness and self-reflection are what help us still the "committee of idiots" or the myriad of thoughts that run through and whirl around in the mind. You have to be still and reflect. This is when your mind has no particular thoughts; it is in a state of pure awareness. You allow yourself simply to be. Stillness and self-reflection give you inner growth when you reach an expanded state of mental and spiritual development. It helps you get rid of old thought patterns, rigid habits of thinking and feeling. This kind of thinking makes you depressed. They are distractions from reality. Look at finding where your thoughts come from. Are they coming from past thinking, other people's thinking, or your own confused thinking? They can come from a place of peace and silence by going within.

Negative influences of the mind: fear, anger, greed, compulsiveness, doubt, and other negative emotions. Negative attitudes turn into chemical toxins called "stress hormones" that are linked to different diseases, such as, cancer, heart problems, colitis, and hypertension to name a few.

Stillness and self-reflection assists us to find bliss, inner harmony, and centeredness. It is the only way to find the peace within and to connect to it so that we can live it. **Peace can never be found or experienced outside of oneself.** It is found when we learn to control our mental and emotional bodies and stay centered within. Stillness and self-reflection teaches us how to master this state of mind, and once we do, we discover new energies.

The health benefits of stillness and self-reflection are the lowering of high cholesterol levels. Cholesterol is a primary risk factor for heart attacks because excess cholesterol in the blood is directly lined to the fatty plaque deposits that clog the arteries leading to the heart. Blood, of course, is our lifeline because it carries oxygen, another form of energy to the body's cells. Clogged arteries means there is little oxygen circulating.

How to Achieve Stillness and Do Self-Reflection

To achieve stillness and to do self-reflection, you will need to slow the brain wave activity to the **alpha state.** People in the alpha brain wave state have more creativity and physical relaxation. The level of stress is reduced and many people enter a light or hypnoidal trance. At this level there is a slowing down of brain and body pulsation.

The information below suggests how to achieve stillness and self-reflection under ideal circumstances. Most of us are not able to find these conditions at work, so a second set of instructions will be offered.

1. Wait two hours after you have eaten.
2. Sit with your spine straight in a comfortable chair. Some people like to sit on a pillow or rug with their legs crossed.
3. Breathe deeply and rhythmically, inhaling through your nose, while your chest and solar plexus both expand. The solar plexus is located two inches below your naval. Exhale through your mouth, pushing up gently from your solar plexus.
4. Hold the air within for a few seconds before exhaling. Focus your attention on any part of your body that is holding tension and release the tension outward.
5. With eyes closed visualize white light above your head. Bring it down slowly to expand and fill your entire body with the white light. Try to hold your full concentration on the light until you can visualize every cell in your body filled with this high-energy frequency.

6. While visualizing the white light within, allow all thoughts to pass through your mind. Hold your vision on the white light.

Stages of Stillness and Self-Reflection

Stage I Concentration

This stage of concentration requires discipline over our thoughts and actions. Staring at any object, such as a burning candle, a flower, or a still lake, for several seconds, without blinking, will enhance deep concentration.

Stage II Contemplation

The contemplative stage requires the ability to focus internally. You might choose visualizing the light within, for example. When our thoughts become clear and purer, we say, "The light just came on." It dissolves all that is not of the highest, and it is a transforming power.

Stage III Stillness and Self-Reflection

When you are completely still, you will be able to receive whatever it is that you need—renewed energy, answers, and peace. While we know that this is true, we do an amazing number of energy wasting things before we resort to being still. Take just a minute and scan your body. Look in a mirror or feel the tense muscles in your face. Feel the tightness in the muscles at the back of your neck. They will actually hurt when you touch them. Check out the rest of your body. Is your heartbeat racing? Do you have a headache? Are your eyes squinting? Is your body moving with flow or does it feel disconnected? Are you able to communicate your thoughts with the exact words and feelings you want to express?

While you are at work, take some five minute breaks. Do whatever it takes to have this uninterrupted time because you deserve it, and it is necessary to replenish your energy. Take your phone off the hook, lock your door, find a place to be alone, and get still. Let people know that you need to replenish your energies. Free your hands of all objects. Let the business thoughts pass through your mind. Say a word of your choosing over and over so that thoughts do not enter your mind.

Four Self-Reflection Exercises

1. ***The induction of spontaneously experienced colors.***
   How does this work? We know that proper breathing increases our energy, enables our minds to become clear, and then, we can think the thoughts we desire. In reading about the "stars" in our bodies, the metabolic energy centers, we learned that we can increase the energy flow to places where we are weak. We learned that we can use our mind energy to produce whatever color we choose. If you want to be more assertive, you would choose to focus on red, if you wanted to be more spiritual, you would focus on purple, if you wanted to heal, you would think about green, the new growth color. You have the ability to project whatever thought, feeling, and emotion you wish. It is visible in the colors in your electromagnetic field, your aura. The first time I

attended a class where the teacher said to breathe in a color, I thought like you probably are now. *She is nuts!* But the color I chose was green and at that time it was the color I needed most because I was still healing from cancer surgery. By the way, the color that shines from me most of the time is green because I am an emotional and physical healer. In my classes, I have taught my students to pick a color and then to imagine it and to feel that color. When they stand in front of the group under the favorable conditions of an off-white wall and fairly good lighting, the class can all see the color they have chosen. You do this all the time but maybe don't know it. Say you had a favorite yellow dress or shirt that you wore when you were a kid or at a particular meaningful occasion, seeing that color would trigger specific images or emotions. You've seen characters in the movies change totally at the sight, sound or smell of something that brought back fond memories.

2. *The visualization of concrete objects*
Some of us do a better job at self-reflection and meditation when we have a concrete object to relate to because it gives us a starting point or reminds us of a specific place or a particular association. A sand pail might remind you of the ocean.

3. *The experience of selected feeling-states*
We can access our feeling states whenever we want to. People are taught to associate their desired feeling states by touching a part of their body or going there in their mind. For instance, you could choose to remember how it feels to kiss your beloved by associating it with rubbing the back of your hand. If you choose to go there in your mind, you could remember touching the person, how they smelled, what they looked like, and how they sounded.

4. *The elicitation of specific information from the unconscious*

We all have memories buried so deep that we only have brief glimpses into our past. Self-reflection is the means to access these memories, or it is a way that we can decide not to let the memories have power over us. Say you have an unknown fear of water because your parents failed to tell you that you almost drowned as a baby. You can choose to feel powerful and overcome the fear. More information would surface from the unconscious if we were more aware and not fearful of the information it would reveal.

How to Visualize the Goal

You've heard seminar speakers talk several times about the importance of writing your goals. This book is not going to spend the energy convincing you of the necessity of doing this, but hopefully, it is going to teach you the necessary ingredient to make your goal writing a success—visualization. At this point in the book, you have learned the following about visualization. It is a right brain activity that enables you to see the possible **and the impossible**. So, if you can conceive of an idea, you can achieve it. You have learned to access information from outside of yourself, from the intelligence of the universe, by being still and doing meditation. **You can do what many of the inventors, writers, artists, and great thinkers have done.** The second thing you have learned is that the individual cells in your body have memory and they can remember how to do something successfully if you visualize in your mind what it is that you want to do. If you are shooting at a target and you focus too much on how to do it, you will not do as well because you will be interfering with your body's natural activity. You will find that it is more effective to think about the desired outcome. This is sort of a negative example, but it illustrates my point. Children who have been playing games on video where they shoot at a target are so practiced that when then find a gun in the house, they are able to shoot another child so strategically that they kill them. The right side of our brain is so effective that simply being shown how to do something helps us imagine how to do it. We call it an engram when we have memories of how specific muscular actions have *felt.* They initiate and control new movements by selecting and rearranging learned movements. This memory of the feeling enables you to remember the accomplishment rather than the instruction. We call it ***being in the zone*** when we become so at ease doing something because we are so involved in doing the thing, we don't even have to think what we are doing.

A couple of other things about goals. Most of us cannot see our strengths, and secondly, we develop our strengths as we are doing our goals. We become more powerful and more energetic when we release our self-judgment. Of course, you can do **it** if you can honestly visualize yourself doing it. Remember, the mind can only relate to what it already knows. Looking at the results before they actually happen enables you to *see* what it is you want.

The Principle of Detachment

> Attachment is the great fabricator of illusions; reality can be attained only by someone who is detached.
>
> Simone Weil

Detachment from Memories

Our attachment to things, people, ideas, places, beliefs—that pretty much covers it all—keeps us from being productive and in high energy. Below are some statements highlighted in bold type. I invite you to think about each of them, and then list on a piece of paper the specific things you are holding on to. Each time you detach from your attachments you grow closer to being who you are rather than the idea who you want to be. When you are simply "being," you are not even conscious of it.

Detachment is an inside job and part of the process of being truthful about yourself. Detachment is the answer to the question in the introduction, **"How does suppression of emotions rob your energy and create mood disorder?"** Emotions are feelings and as long as you hold on to a feeling about something you are still *tied* to. Anything you are tied to you are still giving it your energy. Letting go is what you must do in order to be totally free. It is takes more energy to stay attached to something than it is to believe that there is a benefit from letting it go. What is the first thing you do when you detach? You see what is wrong, followed by seeing what is right.

Attachment to the past is:

Holding on to dreams of what might have been.

Several years ago the book, *Bridges of Madison County,* stayed on the best seller's list for some time and then it was made into a movie. The simple plot was about a mid-west housewife who met a photographer taking pictures of covered bridges while her husband and children were out of town at the state 4H meet.

The short romance between Angelique, the housewife, and Robert Kinkaid, was written as accidental and continued in the minds of the characters when Kinkaid left town. The author had both characters spend the rest of their lives remembering the *dream* of their romance and the story had readers in tears until the end of the book. Angelique played the victim role, a self-sacrificing wife, who once a year drug out physical remembrances of the weekend. Robert never loved again, and at his death had his few worldly possessions sent to Angelique in a box. My critique of the characters was simply, who couldn't stay in love with someone you only knew for a week? And, what wasted lives and wasted energy those two spent remembering a romance based on *what they thought it might have been?* What are we holding on to with no way of knowing how it would have turned out?

Detachment is letting go of people or places.

Many people stay so attached to happy memories of people and places that it prevents them from receiving new and better experiences. Some people believe that there is a limit on how much good they deserve and can expect. They say after the death of their spouse, "I had a good marriage for blank years, so I can't expect more," or "I've experienced so much success in business, it can't go on forever." **They are attached to the idea of limitedness.**

Oprah Winfrey got a great lesson on the cost of attachment from Gary Zukov, author of *Seat of the Soul.* As a guest on the show, Zukov was talking about the different ways we use food and other things to cover up our feelings. "Our abuse of these things," he said, "is a symptom that we feel powerless." Oprah revealed that after she realized that her movie, *The Beloved,* was not going to be a success and that people were not going to see it, she ate a lot of macaroni and cheese and bread pudding. Here's a woman worth a billion dollars, the most influential woman in the U.S., and she still couldn't make people go see this movie. Frequently, she mentions the movie so she's still attached to the outcome. It is defining her, she thinks. You could see the light go on for her when she realized that she became so attached to the outcome of the movie that its failure made her feel powerless. She believed her power was external so she felt powerless. This was also a great lesson for me.

Attachment to old failures keeps us experiencing the same things over and over, while we half-heartedly say we wish for success.

We get attached to expecting or learning to live with lowered expectations. I heard a great baseball story about Tommy Lasorda coaching a minor league team before he coached in the major leagues. His team had lost seven straight games in a row. Lasorda was trying to think how he could boost the team's morale and improve their self-image when he read in the newspaper about a team that was considered to be the greatest team in history. He asked his team, "Did you also hear that this team lost nine games in a row?" They said, "No." It took Lasorda's team two more losing games to change their attitude, but they did, and they ended up having a winning season. Asked later, if it were true that the best team actually lost nine games, Lasorda said, "No." He replied, "I only asked if they *knew*." What are you telling yourself that you have no way of knowing whether it will be true or not?

Take a minute and look at your bag of accumulated *failures* and *defeats* that take so much of your effort to lug around on your back or drag around on the ground. When you go back and look at many things that you worked so hard to achieve and yet failed, are you now happy you weren't successful getting what you thought you wanted? This applies to lost loves too.

Attachment to believing that we are *right* about something takes a lot of energy.

First, we spend a lot of time and energy just making sure we were right in being detached. Second, we hold a lot of conversations in our mind chatter convincing ourselves that we have made the right decision. Third, we feel that we must find someone to agree with decisions…that we have already made. Ah, the time we spend telling our stories to our friends in search of the person who unequivocally agrees with us. When we go inward for our answers we don't have to confirm with anyone.

"Are you tired of defending your position to others?"

Time after time, my best friend keeps bringing up things in my life, *that she thinks that I should do.* Each time, I patiently explain to her that all my actions are based on my belief that I am *staying on purpose.* I had to explain myself to her again today. It made me wonder what am I saying or doing wrong so that I am battling over this same ground? Then I realized that her behavior is the *effect.* The *cause* is that I have ineffectually communicated my position or she has not chosen to receive the communication. This has given me the opportunity to ask myself, "Am I showing a lack of conviction?" and "Am I coming from my weaknesses, instead of my strengths?" People justify trying to tell you what to do by telling you that they are concerned about you. What they are "lovingly" telling you is that they don't think that you know what you are doing–that you are weak. My decision now is to come from my strengths, to nip it in the bud, as Barney Fife would say. It has just become very **clear** that every time I am fighting over this *ground* again it is taking my energy. Now, how do I know without a doubt that I am making the right choices, besides the obvious statement, that no one has the right to tell you what to do? Well, I am practicing what I am telling you to do in this book...and that is ***being energy***. I am not acting *like* I am an energy being. Being energy, means, that my strength comes from letting energy move through me without blockages. It means that I can intuitively know everything that I need to know. It is not obnoxious to say this. After all, who better than you should know what you should do? You are going to be held accountable for what you do.

Detachment is the Decision to Live from True Intelligence.

We put a lot of energy into proving that somebody else is wrong while it really doesn't make any difference. We also put a lot of energy into trying to find solutions to our old problems. If something continues to be a problem over and over, is it something you want in your life? Doesn't holding on to a problem say that you have a need for a problematic life? Are you always saying to yourself, "Why are these things always happening to me?" Shouldn't you be asking yourself, "What are my beliefs and thinking processes that keep attracting painful situations into my life?" The first step is finding out how to know things differently so that you can do things differently. Different use of your mind energy will produce different results. A woman in a class I taught said that she had been angry with a friend for dying and leaving her. When she saw the effect of holding that anger and how it was keeping her in a low vibration, she gave up the anger.

Detachment is Choosing to be Self-evident.

When a person is self-evident, being as they were created, they choose to see their weaknesses and then they choose to let them go. They have the ability to see the problems for what they are. This enables them to see the solutions. As our understanding of any problem or situation increases, we can act from a higher level. Our answers come from seeing the cause of the problems instead of focusing on the effects. Think back to the worst thing you were attached to, maybe the breakup of a marriage. Do you remember how much relief you felt when you decided that you didn't want to hurt anymore and you just released the attachment to anger? You made a decision not to suffer…to be happy. It was the only choice you could make and to your surprise detachment became effortless.

We hear too much said about fear, instead of having a sense of self, which is not fearful. Here's hopefully, some new insight into *fear.* The people that we are most fearful of are the least powerful or they would not find the need to project fear. Look back at the scary conditions you faced. Wasn't it your reaction to the condition that was the real fear? When we relate to something like fears we get to think that we are fear and this is what limits us. Look at how most people react when their company announces changes in policy, in procedure, in anything. The fear resides within them.

Attachment and judgment to outcomes keeps us from receiving all the blessings or good that we might receive. This applies to people, projects, and plans. Do you find yourself having to defend your actions to yourself and others? Do you find yourself making decisions based on fear? Can you make intelligent choices, if they are made in a worried or anxious state? These are decisions made from weakness rather than strength. If you have made your choices from self-reflection, you will **know** that you have made the right decision.

Anything You have to Control, Controls You.

Got a problem controlling your temper? Look at how much effort, how much breath control, how much muscle and fist clinching goes into controlling temper. These are the effects. The controlling *cause* is being tied, attached to an expectation of people or outcomes.

Anyone who is a parent can relate to this. The way to win here is to be in charge, not always in conflict with your child. Those who practiced that when their children were small had fewer problems with their teenagers.

The worst control that we place on ourselves is worrying about what other people think. This is what our mother told us in high school. But right at this moment, if we are honest, we can list five people we are giving our power to by worrying what they are thinking or trying to get them to see how we are right and they are wrong. In each of these situations we should ask, "Is what I am feeling about that person good for **me or them** right now?" Observe a person who hears just the name of someone they are angry with and their whole body flares up. Remember the section on neurotransmitters? Any negative chemicals you are sending to your cells are entering them and causing negative changes.

Recent surveys show that Americans are working longer than people from any other industrial nation. We work two weeks more than the Japanese do. The German worker gets ten weeks of vacation, and the French get eight. While we are the most productive, our rate of discontent is considerably higher. We can not experience personal happiness in the achievement of our success if there are things that also cause us pain. Many workers say that they are *driven* by money to work longer and more. Then the money or success that drives them is doing the controlling. So many people live miserable lives during their younger years because they believe that they will enjoy their retirement years. The problem is, they never reach their retirement years.

As humans we have the ability to make choices in our lives. The voluntary muscles of our bodies enable us to make conscious movements based on cellular memory. Also, we have behavior patterns we may choose. We receive sensory information whether we want it or not. Other information we have to make conscious effort to receive. When we put forth this "effort," we gain a sense of ourselves and objects.

Our mind, contained in our 100 trillion cells, is conditioned for good or bad by our thoughts. Usually when we think of thought, we relate to analytical thought and conscious arrangement of sequences. Other thought forms, like feeling states—sensory memories, kinetic melodies, focused imaginings—are more involved in our motor behavior. We can choose thought forms that produce successful coordination and control.

How to Change Our States of Being

Our internal representations are structured through our senses: auditory, visual, kinesthetic, olfactory, and taste. We remember the face of a loved one, the smells of Christmas, the feel of the leather in a new car, the taste of a big juicy steak. We can change our internal representations by changing what they represent. You can change the effect of any experience life has upon you. We call this reframing.

All of us can relate to the experience of a broken relationship. Our state of being at the time of the breakup contained many of the following elements, a sense of loss, anger, shock, sadness, relief, stress, disbelief, or peacefulness. Every time you remember this event, you also recall the emotional feelings or you couldn't remember it. You can choose to look at and feel differently about the experience if you don't want to relive the experience. First, figure out how you get into your negative states. What do you do with your body? What do you do with your thinking? How do you feel?   At the time of the breakup you may have felt that this person was the last person you would ever love. You were mad or felt anger. You felt bad every time you thought about them even though you've moved on and found someone better suited for you.   Now you know that you can use your mental energy to change the internal representations that normally produce states of unresourcefulness (lack of energy) and causes them to automatically trigger new internal representations that put you in a resourceful state.

We are walking billboards. The way we react or feel about our experiences is communicated through external and internal communications, our words, tonalities, facial expression, body language, and physical actions. If you will pay attention to a person, you can know everything about them.

Helen Keller was quoted as saying, "The touch of some hands is an impertinence. I have met people so empty of joy, that when I clasped their fingertips, it seemed as if I were shaking hands with a northeast storm. Others have sunbeams in them, so that their grasp warms my heart."

The state we are in determines how we feel about our actions in the present and what actions we take. If we do something incorrectly but we are in a good mood, it certainly doesn't affect us the way it would if we were in a bad mood. The two things that cause our states are our physiology (body) and our submodalities—seeing, hearing, smelling, feeling and tasting. All of us know that to feel good we must have good posture, take deep breaths to get oxygen in our cells, and make sure our bodies are not chemically unbalanced with sugar, cigarettes, or alcohol. A smile on our face not only changes our attitude, but the attitude of others.   We know that the more we increase bodily activity the more endorphins are created which gives us a good feeling. Our submodalities create the way we feel internally. We use our senses in our external world and internal world.

Before we talk about detachment, will you take a moment and look at again your list of the five people you are angry with? List them according to the person you are angriest at first and then on down. Start by thinking about the top person, remember how you felt emotionally when you were the angriest at them. Just the mention of their name will probably start you muttering some choice words.

Now let's look at what is happening to you. First, the fact that you listed the person shows that you are still tied to them. We have learned that thoughts are energy. So, your choosing to merely think of the person expends your mental energy. The thought of them probably still makes your blood pressure rise, an indication that you are tightening and constricting your muscles and getting red faced. You have stopped your ability to think or act productively. Second, your ability to recall the feeling tells you that you have stored negative memories. This starts the production of chemicals that are traveling all over your body and entering all of your cells. You have increased the production of killer cells and lowered your immune system. Bottom line, what you have done is depleted your energy without any positive results in return. If you go through the other four names in the same way, you will probably have a heart attack and not finish reading the book. Staying tied to any anger does not serve you because **attachment is suffering**. You can choose to let go of anger and other negative thoughts as quickly as they come. We create an ego or individual self made up of all of our ideas, identities, thoughts, opinions, grudges, unresolved expressions, motives, wounds, angers, fears, hopes, dreams, and loyalties. These become our self-image rather than the essential self or the real self, which is who you really are.

Attachment to the future and outcomes is just as harmful. For example, maybe you have been the manager of a very important project from your company, worked devotedly for three months, and done all the planning and implementation humanly possible. Now there is nothing left for you to do, except worry. What a waste of energy! This is the time to replenish your energies and then focus them elsewhere. When we stay attached to anything, we run the risk of constricting it and stopping it from being more than anything we expected.

Learn to Recognize and Balance Your Extremes.

Have you ever envied or desired to be like those really "high energy" people who occasionally have extreme feelings of joy and happiness? I have. What I learned though is that those people experience extreme states on both ends. Their extreme joy and happiness is offset with extreme sorrow and sadness. It is better to be able to see the whole picture because nothing is without responsibility and a cost. Let's say your focus for the last year has been a new bigger sales territory. You are ecstatic when you get it but later you find that you are having to travel more, meet higher expectations, and give more of your physical energy. Your sadness will be at the same level of your happiness because you did not take the time to see the whole picture. This doesn't mean that new challenges aren't good but we have to expect initial changes.

Trauma leaves a cellular memory or an energetic impression that subconsciously effects one's life if not dealt with. *Mechanisms of Memory*, author E. Roy John, a neurophysilogist, reveals that the same brain cells are used when an individual first sees an object and is later asked to remember that same object. Our personalities, behaviors and health are affected by our memories that are stored in cellular memories and our subconscious. For these reasons we need to release stored negative energies (memories) in our cells and in our stars, through bodywork and consciousness (awareness) through the five senses. Consciousness helps our world come alive.

Dr. Arthur Janov in, *Why You Get Sick, How You Get Well,* says the stronger the emotion in an event the stronger the memory of that event and, paradoxically, the more likely it will not be remembered consciously. According to a *Science News* article by James McGaugh of the University of California, Irvine, "Intense feelings triggered by a stressful or emotional event help preserve memories of that experience, in large part by activating... (adrenergic) stress hormones responsible for storing emotionally charged information."

A ten-year-old girl received a heart transplant from another young girl who was murdered. The transplant recipient reported having dreams of the specific details of the other girl's murder. A woman who received a heart and lung transplant from a young man strangely began having cravings for beer and Chicken McNuggets, even though she didn't previously like beer and was a vegetarian who didn't eat chicken or fried foods. After meeting the young man's family, she learned of his favorites—beer and Chicken McNuggets. She also dreamed of things and people that were totally unknown to her. Other transplant recipients reported similar stories. Another proof that our cells have memory is shown when we receive an immunization. The body's defense cells are activated to kill intruding virus and bacteria.

Actually, if we depend on our five senses for all our knowing, we will always limit our knowing to what is just around us. The reality behind the phenomenal world is not through the physical senses but through deep intuition. The word is derived from the Latin *intueri,* and means "to consider, to look on," suggesting some outside vantage-point. Jung said, "When we exercise our intuition, we experience a deeply satisfying sense of having done things right."

The Principle of Awareness

How many times have you said, "I wasn't aware of the problem?"
How many times do we turn up the music, the TV, or the noise in our minds?
How many times do we look in the mirror at our bodies, yet we don't pay attention to what our bodies are telling us?

Awareness permits people, companies, and organizations to have a sense of flow. People with awareness excel in diagnosis, examination, actualization, prognostics, and channeling. It promotes a shift in our thinking and in our behaviors. Awareness immediately gives us access to the best procedures, the best answers, and the most efficient methods. The aware person is the one who always has a laser like precision sense of knowing. They know when to listen, when to take action, and when to wait. Awareness helps us be attuned by using our senses, higher sensory perceptions, intuitive abilities, inspired thinking, and writing.

It helps us to stop operating from the "I hoped it would work out" methodology to using our creative thinking. It helps us to plan so that we either get results or the "reasons why not." Awareness alerts our attention immediately to a lack of direction, energy, and success in personal relationships, communications, procedures, thinking, perceptions, and negotiations. Because awareness enables us to see the situation from the other person's point of view, we can know how to get to the heart of the matter, the person, or situation. Actually you can know and be aware if someone is being truthful.

People with awareness:

* Become proactive
* Realize that life is based on choices
* Set goals which predetermine their destiny
* Have desires and dreams
* Are altruistic
* They learn to recognize problems early, so that they don't operate from a sense of chaos. They don't wait for tragedies to force change. They don't rely on emergency contingencies. They have a sense of "ah ha" instead of "oh, no."
* They aren't afraid to take risks because they have premeditated their actions and the results.

The Principle of Wholeness

Everything that flows can be considered as healthy. Strain is only experienced if congestion and blockages hinder the flow, regardless of the cause of these blockages...Disease is a reflection of the inner; it is the opposite of health. Health is usually associated with joy, happiness, and a pain-free life; with having ideas and being able to live them out; with being active and being able to laugh; with being able to perceive and recognize things others cannot or choose not to see. Disease means frustration, pain, and the paralysis of life. Disease is walking on a wrong path, or one that has been taken only because the right path, or one that has been taken only because the right path could not be recognized...There is only one simple road to well-being: one's own path.
—**Peter Mandel**

People who live with constant stress do not feel in control of their lives. Life for them is a constant fear battle and leads to health problems. Men from suffer from alcoholism, workalcoholism, emotional withdrawal, broken relationships, violence, and physical problems such as high blood pressure and heart attacks. Health problems for women include eating disorders, low self-esteem, the "superwoman" syndrome, overconcern for others, emotional dependence, and physical problems such as premenstrual syndrome and headaches. If you have a lot of headaches, you need to be aware that your scalp and forehead are very tense probably because you are chronically contracting the muscles in the forehead. Chronic raising of the eyebrows causes headaches at the front of the head. When we knit the muscles between our eyebrows as we worry a lot or as we focus narrowly on our work, we create deep lines. They represent the stress that worry causes and are just another form of muscle constriction. Tension in the muscles of the neck also cause headaches in the same location. Abnormal, chronic anxiety occurs when a person responds anxiously when there is no real threat.

Treatment for stress, anxiety and depression: Relaxation and meditation talk therapy, dietary changes and vitamin therapy, biofeedback, exercise, herbs, and bodywork.

Stress and the Immune System

Stress causes us to be unhealthy because it keeps our immune system from functioning properly. First, we need to note the characteristics of the immune system.

1. The immune system has an innate ability to recognize which cells belong to its body.
2. Once exposed to a specific antigen (bacteria, viruses) the system never forgets the experience.
3. The thymus gland into transforms T-cells into fully functional cells. They patrol for potentially dangerous microbes. They provide protection against cancer. The thymus hurries along immune cells to maturity as T-cells: the more thymosin secreted, the more T-cells sent out.
4. B-cells manufacture antibodies that are specifically directed against foreign antigen.
5. White blood cells can make chemicals that are practically identical to certain peptides that the nervous system produces. The brain and the immune system both react to stress by using some of the same chemicals.

According to a 1996 report published by Yankelovich Partners, 33 percent of all Americans feel their job is more stressful than a year ago. The American Institute of Stress reports that 78 percent of all Americans describe their job as more stressful, with more than two-thirds stating that their job has gotten more stressful during the last five years.

Occupational Health and Safety News and the National Council on Compensation Insurance estimate that $95 billion in annual costs is related to lost work productivity and that companies spend another $26 billion on stress-related medical and disability payments. The National Center for Health Statistics reports that, on average, women feel more stress than men and that men and women with more education and higher incomes feel higher levels of stress due largely to their increased financial and managerial responsibilities.

One reason animals and people are unable to respond beyond a certain point under stress is that their reservoirs of norepinephrine and possibly other biochemicals vital to normal body activities are drained dry in response to the excessive challenge. We describe people as being drained by an activity. There is a distinct difference between the vitality of natural killer cells in **good copers** compared to those of **poor copers**. Biochemical aftershock of emotional states sways the immune system. Response to minor daily insults and hassles can also affect the immune system. Research suggests that the way individuals perceive these onslaughts on their sanity and health makes a great difference to the body's response. The mind has its own homeostasis and struggles constantly to maintain an emotional balance to keep peace and health within. Although two people in the same place at the same time may ostensibly have the same experience, the significant influence on its outcome is the person's perception of the event: the individual's subjective degrees of control, capacity to manage the situation.

The Broken Heart Study showed that many spouses die soon after the death of their spouse. Their white blood cells became less responsive. People with multiple personalities show us the power of our minds. Certain illnesses only appear when certain personalities appear. For example, a man had specific allergic reactions to citrus fruit only when certain personalities dominated. A woman who had multiple personalities said that she only had diabetes when a certain personality appeared. Other people with multiple personalities have some personalities who have to wear glasses while others don't.

Hypertension and high cholesterol are additional ways in which our body chemistry reacts to excessive stress. Hypertension is called the silent killer and causes heart attack and stroke. An estimated 30 million people have borderline hypertension. Even a small rise in blood pressure is considered extremely dangerous in the long run. Insurance companies use blood pressure as the most significant indicator of life expectancy. You can extend your life by sixteen years with normal blood pressure.

Stress causes muscles to go into spasms that grip the nerves and vessels. This reduces circulation of blood to other areas of the body and can lead to pain and disease. Disease exits in relation to the absence of ease. Our adaptive mechanism becomes weakened under prolonged nervous anxiety. Creative people are only as great as the size of their thinking. One's own destructive habits are the greatest obstacles to personal success.

Do you remember when people thought acupuncture was weird? The very idea of people sticking needles into people's bodies and talking about pressure points seemed ridiculous. Doctors from the East teach us that we have twenty basic pathways, meridians that are all interconnected. The meridians trace a complete energy circle within the body every 24 hours. Several hundred acupoints give direct access into the meridian energy flow. We began hearing from people who were relieved of pain that they had suffered for years. Today acupuncture is commonplace.

Now the public is now demanding that Holistic and Traditional Medicine become integrated. Hospital Association annual conferences are having speakers on Energy Medicine. Reike is used before and after surgery. The Holistic Nurses Association and other groups have taught thousands of nurses how to use Therapeutic Touch with their patients.

Carl Jung said that we carry an archetype of wholeness within us, which is always at work to bring us toward fullness and self-realization. When the body's energy channels and centers are open, energy flows freely and unobstructed giving the person a fluid sense of wholeness that includes good physical health, emotional balance, mental clarity and spiritual well-being which results from being in tune with one's own soul and the spirit of nature.

Happiness is what we feel when our biochemicals of emotions, the neuropeptides and their receptors, are open and flowing freely throughout the psychosomatic network, integrating and coordinating our systems, organs, and cells in a smooth and rhythmic movement. Happiness is our natural state because we are hardwired for bliss. Only when our systems get blocked, shut down, and disarrayed do we experience the mood disorders that add up to unhappiness.

Unfortunately, most people live in a state of depression rather than wholeness. Twenty-five percent of adult women and twelve percent of men—more than seventeen million people suffer from major depression. They have continuing feelings of sadness, despondency, and hopelessness and ultimately that life is not worth living. Some of the causes of depression are: prolonged physical illness, an seemingly unresolvable dilemma like not being able to leave an unhealthy relationship, a side affect of certain drugs, a series of losses such as home, job, and loved ones. Patients many times are not warned that surgery, anesthesia, and chemotherapy imbalance your body chemistry and cause depression. Depressed people either lose their appetite or become compulsive eaters. A deficient diet that doesn't give a person energy leaves him without activity and in isolation.

Depression is anger turned inward. It may stay unexpressed, buried below consciousness, where it seems to be controlled. Slowly, however, it will implode. We have been taught in our culture to we keep our feelings hidden. We are afraid to express them honestly for fear others will be indifferent to our sorrows or alienated and hurt by our anger. We tell ourselves that it is better to deny feelings, to suppress them, go through the emotions of happiness and pretend to have fun—until the day the bottom falls out. Finally something happens that is too big to be suppressed and we realize that we are in a state of depression.

Depression creates low energy. People who feel powerless stay in a state of hopelessness by pretending that they don't care about the things that they really do. People in this state of gloom prefer to be alone, avoiding what *is*. They prefer a self-punishing behavior of blame for how things are because they see no way to make changes. A feeling of loss creates emptiness and the decision to reject the feeling rather than letting it go keeps us from healing. Unhealed feelings are the accumulation of bruised and broken emotions. In order to heal one must mourn the loss and *feel the feeling* rather than holding on to the loss.

Signs of Depression

✳ Persistent feelings of sadness, helplessness
✳ Loss of interest or pleasure in normal activities, including sex
✳ Decreased or increased sleep
✳ Decreased or increased appetite with weight loss or gain
✳ Decreased energy, fatigue, and lethargy
✳ Difficulty concentrating, remembering, or making decisions
✳ Restlessness and irritability
✳ Thoughts of death or suicide
✳ Various pains, such as headaches or chest pain that are not accompanied by any evidence of disease

The immune systems of depressed people are less responsive than those of normal individuals. Many women incur breast cancer soon after a divorce. The adrenal glands in depressed individuals produce unusually large amounts of corticosteroids Many people seek relief through prescribed drugs that cause unnecessary side effects and health risks. They do not seek the underlying problems causing the depression. James Gordon, MD. author of *Manifesto for a New Medicine: Your Guide to Healing Partnerships and the Wise Use of Alternative Therapies,* says, "Depression is a process of growth, not an aberration. People need human help through such a period."

Instead, people choose to take the quick, easy way out by taking antidepressants. Prozac's sales the first year were $350 million—more than the total sum previously spent annually by Americans on all antidepressants combined. Prozac zeroes in on the neurotransmitter serotonin. Sales are now at a billion dollars despite murder and suicide related incidents.

Some Prozac users who become unsettled at their newfound happiness incur what is called uplift anxiety. Such people typically grieve for their former selves because their most fundamental aspect, unhappiness, has been taken away. We have been taught that we can't be happy all the time.

Dr. Norman Shealy believes all illness is related to depression. When we are depressed, we can only think about our own negative thoughts. This negative mind energy keeps the body from maintaining health. Light impacts both mood and immunity by affecting neurohormonal and neurochemical behaviors. Light is currently being used to augment psychiatric and cancer medication.

The drug cimetidine, known as Tagamet, was the largest selling prescription medication in the U.S. It is a "miracle drug" used to treat hyperacidity and ulcers. Gastritis, indigestion, gas, and pain and bleeding are the prices we pay for the fact that we channel feeling into the gastro-intestinal tract. The mouth, the esophagus, the duedenum and small intestine, and colon are included in the gastro-intestinal tract. Diseases as a result are esophagitis, esophageal spasm, peptic ulcers, duodenitis, and irritable bowel syndrome

It has been discovered that many peptide hormones, previously thought to be found only in the G-I tract, have also been found in the brain, among which are vasoactive intestinal polypeptide, cholecystokinin, gastin, substance P, neurotensin, enkaphalins, insulin, glucagon, bombesin, secretin, somtostatin, and thyro-tropin-releasing hormone. The only reason all these are listed is to show you the large number. The fact that the stomach and the brain make the same hormones, which are chemical messengers, and that they share receptor sites for these chemicals, provides a way for them to "talk" to each other. But you knew that the first time you felt *butterflies in your stomach.*

These kinds of drugs are thought to correct an imbalance of the brain's neurotransmitters, the chemical messengers that produce different emotional and mental states. Our bodies produce serotonin. Adequate levels of **serotonin** boost our feelings of optimism, well being, self-esteem, relaxation, and security. It improves concentration, heightens perception, moods, vision, gastrointestinal functioning, and memory.

When serotonin levels are low, a person has trouble sleeping and concentrating; he feels confused, alone, isolated, unloved and unworthy of love; he may think of suicide or become violent. Some other side effects are anxiety, blackouts, insomnia, impaired judgment, nightmares, and sexual dysfunction. Quite a price to pay! This is the reason that we should not be judgmental of people who have a chemical imbalance. They need our help instead.

Adequate levels of the chemical neurotransmitters, **dopamine** and **norepinephrine** increase feelings of alertness, assertiveness, wakefulness, and willpower. They heighten energy, they improve muscle coordination. They even speed up our thought process. A shortage causes lethargy, weakness, and a kind of vegetative depression. Drugs that boost dopamine and norepinephrine levels are called tricyclic antidepressants. You can finds drugs to alter your brain chemistry but as with most drugs, they carry significant side effects and dangers. Some of the symptoms are diarrhea, nervousness, drowsiness, headache, sweating, insomnia, and anxiety. Others less common are chills, fever, chest pains, nightmares, taste changes, decreased sex drive, painful menstruation, stuffy nose, and tremors.

This is the time to go within and gain insight about what is going on in your life. It is a time that you can powerfully transform your life. The cause could be your belief system, habitual perceptions, physical health, lifestyle habits, or relationships with others. You must deal with the behavior, habit, or perception that caused the depression. You have to take action like changing your diet, seeing a therapist, or exercising—doing anything to move your body.

Other Chemistry Altering Drugs

Anti-depression drugs—Valium, Librium, Prozac, Zoloft, Paxil, Serzone, and Tofranil

Antipsychotic drugs—Haldol, Thorazine, Risperlal, and Clozaril

Not only do these drugs have bad side effects but they block the receptors for **dopamine**. All drugs manufactured outside the body are potentially harmful to the system. All of the body's systems and organs give and receive feedback about what is occurring in the body. It was evident to me even over the phone when a friend of mind was on Prozac because she was very non-reactive. The psychosomatic (mind/body) network operates through a series of delicately balanced feed-back loops involved with the peptides. When chemical information flows freely, it results in homeostasis or balance. We know that brain cells communicate with each other across the synapse. It is at this level that drugs correct chemical imbalances in the brain that are sends out chemicals that bind to the receptor of another. A back up plan is ready to act if too much comes out. The cell has a "re-uptake" mechanism that reabsorbs the excess. We already know that a shortage of the neuro-chemical serotonin secreted by the brain cells creates depression. If this occurs, an antidepressant drug is used to block the re-uptake mechanism, allowing the excess serotonin to flood the receptors, and thereby correct the imbalance. Your intestines are loaded with serotonin receptors. When drugs are used they get overloaded with excess serotonin. Again the body's immune system is compromised because the drugs prevent our natural killer cells from attacking mutated cells.

In the discussion of the body we learned that the hypothalamus is part of the emotional brain, the limbic system. Its neurons have axons, the long, thin tubes that run in the middle of nerve cells and that extend into the pituitary gland. There axons secrete a neuropeptide called **CRF—cortical releasing factor**—which con-trols the release of **ACTH**, an *informational substance* that then travels through the bloodstream to the adrenal glands, where it binds to specific receptors on adrenal glands. This is important because the adrenal glands make steroids called **corticosterone**, a substance that is necessary for healing and damage control when an injury has occurred.

The reason that we are to be in control of our emotions and our attitudes is because stress increases steroid production and makes us physically and emo-tionally unhealthy. Actually, depressed people have high levels of these stress steroids. The glands are not signaled that there are enough steroids in the blood so there is a chronic state of ACTH activation. So the CRF-ACTH production just keeps on making more and more steroids. People who commit suicide have ten times higher levels of CRF. When we recall negative stored childhood memories we have held on to, we stimulate the production of CRF, the peptide of negative expectations.

ACTH is a hormone trigger. It, too, travels to the adrenal glands but via the bloodstream, not the nervous system. At the adrenals it stimulates their outer layer, the cortex. The adrenal cortex releases a barrage of hormones, the corticosteroids. Some, such as cortisone are anti-inflammatory chemicals. They raise the blood sugar present in the body and modulate the body's Immunological defenses. Corticosteroids also act as their own off switches. Once released they make their way through the bloodstream to the pituitary gland.

During stress norepinephrine is released. Even mild stress results in killer-cell activity. A flash of anger and a moment of despair are fleeting events psychologically and physically. Then these emotions linger and become long-term states of mind; they are not so inconsequential, especially when they are negative feelings.

At a certain point, depressed people get stuck in the constant production of CRF and are not able to suppress steroid production. Eventually, there is so much CRF in the system that fluctuations of other peptides throughout the body are curtailed, leaving few other possibilities. We know that our cells retain our bad feelings and stop energy flow. We know that CRF levels increase in highly stressed infants and children. As they grow their receptors for CRF become desensitized, shrinking in size and decreasing in number. Think of what a lifetime of stress does to a person. It goes as far as changing the receptor and then the interior of the cell. These effects can be reversed with unconditional love and hugging. Thank goodness mothers are being taught to massage their babies to regulate and stimulate their natural chemicals. This is also the reason we need to hug and touch people as adults. Those who take the quick way out to overcome anxiety and depression simply don't achieve the levels of intimacy—with their Creator, with others, and with themselves—that people using natural methods can.

Six Ways to Boost Brain Chemistry

Exercise or play a game. Make sure your activity has a sustained level of manageable stress, and sense of tension, then resolution.

Heat it up. Serotonin is released when the brain gets the signal to cool itself down, so try taking a warm bath or sauna.

Find support. Seek out people who will give you a sense of acceptance and unconditional support.

Have sex.

Check out your diet. Eat foods that contain the amino acid tryptophan. Foods such as nuts and bananas, turkey and dairy products.

Find some water. Water infuses nearby air with negative ions, which are known to trigger your brain to release more serotonin.

Health and Emotions

Jacob Liberman says, **"the body has its own wisdom and is a microcosm of a larger macrocosm called nature and the universe.**

We are learning more and more that our chronic diseases are caused from unhealed emotions. Sadness or depression causes the immune cells to send out peptides that increase the buildup of plaque in coronary blood vessels—a key factor in heart attacks. We are finding that our emotional state has much to do with viral attacks. **Because viruses use the same receptors as neuropeptides to enter into a cell, they are able to enter the cell easily if we are in a low energy, depressed state.** The state of our emotions will affect whether or not we succumb to viral infection.

Cancer patients are described as "the long suffering" because they have traits of self-denial stemming from a lack of awareness of their own emotional needs. Sufficient research has shown that cancer patients who keep emotions, such as anger, hidden have slower recovery rates. Actually each of us has a number of tiny cancerous tumors growing in our bodies at every moment. When the flow of peptides is disrupted, our immune system is weakened. The good news is the same immune system has natural killer cells to destroy them and rid the body of cancerous growth. We must put into practice the Principles of Flow, Non-Judgment, Detachment, and Focused Attention to stay healthy.

Energy Medicine refers to hands on healing or healing touch. A hands on healing is an example of a high-energy transfer technique when energy is administered to the body in amounts greater than those that occur naturally. There also can be minimal-energy techniques and self-regulatory techniques. This includes energy-reinforcement techniques such as visualization, hypnosis, meditation, biofeedback, suggestion, placebo, and religious experience healing. These techniques enable the conscious mind to be influenced in a desired direction by the mind. These methods activate preexisting energetic control systems. For instance, the use of suggestion or self-talk enables a person to send the desired thought to the brain which then creates new neural branches resulting in new behaviors or thinking processes.

In physics, a body in motion or a system in a state of operation will continue doing the same thing until an outside force acts upon it to change or "perturb" it. The growth of a tumor cannot be stopped simply by a wish. The cure comes from consciously directing mind energy to change or destroy the individual cancer cells. The cures resulting from these therapies must involve the action of some real force that perturbs the malignant process. The conscious mind in a state of profound belief can control the operation of the body's DC electrical growth-control system and of the immune system to produce the result. Examples of administering external energies to the body are acupuncture and homeopathy.

We are seeing constant new uses of light and laser light in medicine. Thomas Dougherty, M.D., at Roswell Park Memorial Institute, started utilizing light with certain light-sensitive chemicals in the treatment of cancer. Photofrin, a photosensitive chemical was injected into the bloodstream of an individual with cancer. The chemical went throughout the body and collected in all the physical tissues within three days but it began to leave the tissue that was healthy. It seemed to collect within the tissue that had malignant cells in it. Injections were made into people and three days later Dougherty would shine a violet or ultraviolet light on the patient's body. If there were some type of malignant growth somewhere near the skin's surface, that part of the body would fluoresce in response to the light. Dougherty then found that if he took red light, and focused it on the spot, within ten minutes the tumor started to self-destruct. In the last twenty years work has been done on eighteen to twenty different kinds of cancer. Photodynamic Therapy is now done in about seventy to eighty centers within the US.

Light shares with us and everything in the universe that it is both electrical and magnetic. It will become one of the most powerful tools for mindbody healing. It is being used in materialistic medicine, quantum healing and subtle energy medicine.

> The light of the body is your eye; when your eye is clear, your whole body is clear, your whole body is full of light; but when it is bad, your body is full of darkness." The Bible, Luke 11:34

Benefits of Light Therapy

* **Improves retention, information processing and retrieving of new information**
* **Increases verbal fluency**
* **Increases attention and concentration**
* **Impacts your perception and learning processes**
* **Alleviates allergies**
* **Assists your immune system**
* **Reduces stress**
* **Relieves headache and pain**
* **Helps eliminate eye strain**

Light therapy is now being used in integrative medicine to help heal major illness such as cancer, heart problems, diabetes, kidney problems and several other diseases. We are learning that the lack of light and blood cells clumping, a condition known as roulade. Our bodies require food, oxygen and sunlight to live. **Light is the second most important environmental input, after food, in controlling bodily functions.** Thus, a lack of sunlight can lead to disease just as a lack of food, air, and water does. **Ninety-eight percent of sunlight enters through the eyes, while 2% is absorbed through the skin.** After sunbathing there is an increase in cellular oxygen, muscle strength, endurance vitality, and mental stability. Sunlight produces vitamin D and catalyzed other crucial metabolic processes such as the absorption of calcium. Calcium plays a vital role in the transmission of messages in the brain and in the competence of the immune system.

On the one hand, we know that the entire spectrum of natural sunlight is essential for optimal functioning of all living cells in plants, animals, and humans. On the other hand, we humans work in offices using florescent light that lacks full spectrum light and we live without true sunlight. Dr. Richard Wurtman, Professor of Endocrinology at Massachusetts Institute of Technology, states that wavelengths of light are similar to vitamins and minerals since humans also appear to require a broad spectrum of frequencies for physical, emotional and mental well-being. We learned in reading about the "stars," the metabolic energy systems in our bodies, that each wavelength of light that enters the eye has a specific function. **Light ignites the cellular metabolism of our glands and organs in each of the seven areas.** Full spectrum white light and colored light have both shown promising therapeutic applications in the fields of optometry, medicine, psychiatry, psychotherapy, chiropractic, acupuncture, and education.

Historically, sunlight has played an important role in the cure of disease. Patients with tuberculosis were encouraged to sit outdoors in natural light. Until the advent of antibiotics in the late 1930's, the use of sunbathing and ultraviolet light were internationally accepted and commonly utilized medical treatments for a variety of acute bacterial and viral infectious conditions, such as, tuberculosis, viral pneumonia, bronchial asthma, wounds, sores, ulcerations, jaundice, gout, psoriasis, acne, and mumps.

Ever wonder why you get sicker in the winter months? A lack of sunlight impairs the natural defense mechanisms of the body to all forms of stress, both physical and emotional. Also in the winter fertility is lower, fatigue increases, and overall levels of health decline. Winter's darker and shorter daylight hours alter the body's natural internal rhythms, such as the production of hormones and neurotransmitters. People often attempt to "self medicate" during the winter months by increasing their consumption of carbohydrates, alcohol, caffeine, and sugary desserts.

Color in History

There have been references to color as a form of energy throughout this book. Color is now going to be discussed as a healing agent in achieving wholeness.

Color may have been one of the earliest forms of medicine. Historically, the Assyrians, Babylonians, and Egyptians all practiced therapeutic sunbathing. Light was purportedly used for thousands of years by the ancient Egyptians and in the healing temples of Greece. Patients were brought into specifically colored rooms. The windows of these healing rooms were covered with special cloths dyed violet, red, blue, green, etc. In this way, sunlight entering the room gained important qualities to soothe the mind and heal the body.

The Egyptians looked directly into the sun every day and claimed that it would not only heal their physical ailments, but also give them the gift of longevity. They also believed it would open up past memory banks of the observer, almost like a homeopathic remedy. It is as if light would go in and trigger the opening of a part of us that we had kept in the dark.

For millennia sunlight and color have also played an important role in man's spiritual quest. The ancient Greeks and Romans developed sun and air bathing cults. Highly developed rituals for worshipping the rising sun were integral parts of ancient Nordic and Incan cultures. Our ancestors also associated color with their religions and various spiritual practices, whose purpose was to induce mystical states of awareness. Each god and goddess had a special color that depicted their unique powers and qualities. The architects and clergy of the great cathedrals knew about the effects of colored light on the psyche and spirit, as we see in awe inspiring stained glass windows and the colors used in the celebration of religious rituals.

In the last 120 years, physicians and scientists began to document the effects of light and color. In the 1870's scientists discovered that sunlight kills bacteria and other micro-organisms. The "Sun Cure," was prescribed for tuberculosis, cholera, gangrene, diabetes, obesity, chronic gastritis, and hysteria. Sunlamps were used in the 1930's to treat anemia, varicose veins, heart disease, and other degenerative disorders. Dermatologists use small doses of UV to treat herpes and psoriasis, while blue light and full spectrum phototherapy is the treatment of choice for newborns with jaundice.

Medical science is discovering more and more ways to use lasers—coherent light—in surgery. Within the field of psychiatry, full spectrum light is used in the treatment of SAD. Oncologists are already using light to augment the effects of chemotherapy in cancer. Photo-luminescence uses ultraviolet light to sterilize, cook and free it of different bacteria and viruses.

The selection of a color of light that is physically and psychologically uncomfortable for the patient, evokes unconscious conflicts and unresolved traumatic memories stored in the body. Psychological and/or physical trauma are often reflected in physical pain and a variety of psycho-emotional symptoms. It is important for us to look at the color that makes us uncomfortable. This is not the color we don't look good in. This is the one that we have a strong reaction to. It tells us what we are avoiding and what needs to be healed in our-selves. Figure out the color that you hate and then feel the reaction that color evokes in you. That color sym-bolizes what you are lacking in your life.

Kirlian Photography

Kirlian photography is the process of photo-graphing an object by exposing it to a high-frequency electric field. Objects thus photographed are surrounded by discharges of light. The discharges of light may show as blue, orange, red, white, yellow or a combination of these colors. Kirlian images resulted from the aura, or bioplasma, the energy field that surrounds living things. Experiments on photographing objects exposed to an electric field began in the 1890's. Two Russian scien-tists, the husband-and-wife team of Semyou and Valen-tina Kirlian, began developing the modern techniques about 1940.

Most scientists now think the images seen in Kirlian photographs are caused by the following process: The electric field causes the object being photographed to give off electrons. These electrons are accelerated by the electric field and collide with molecules in the air, causing the molecules to separate into positive oxygen and nitrogen ions (charged particles and electrons.) After a sufficient amount of positive ions has built up, the electrons and ions recombine. The recombination of the nitrogen ions and electrons gives off emissions of ultraviolet light. These emissions show up as the discharges of light in the photograph.

Some research indicates that Kirlian image patterns vary according to the subject's emotional, mental, and physical state. Kirlian photographs may be used someday in diagnosing disease or in evaluating a subject psychological state.